GREAT
STORY-POEMS

SUNRISE LIBRARY

GREAT STORY-POEMS

Compiled by Theodoric Jones

Hart Publishing Company, Inc.

NEW YORK CITY

ACKNOWLEDGMENTS

Grateful acknowledgment is made to the copyright owners for permission to reprint the following poems:

"The Cremation of Sam McGee" from *The Collected Poems of Robert Service;* reprinted by kind permission of Dodd, Mead & Company, New York, and The Ryerson Press, Toronto.

"Jean Desprez" from *The Collected Poems of Robert Service;* reprinted by kind permission of Dodd, Mead & Company, New York, and The Ryerson Press, Toronto.

"Blow Me Eyes" from *Nautical Lays of A Landsman* by Wallace Irwin; reprinted by kind permission of Dodd, Mead & Company, New York.

"A Nautical Extravaganza" from *Nautical Lays of A Landsman* by Wallace Irwin; reprinted by kind permission of Dodd, Mead & Company, New York.

"The Stone" from *Collected Poems* by Wilfrid Wilson Gibson, copyright 1926 by Wilfrid Wilson Gibson; reprinted by kind permission of Michael Gibson, Executor of the Estate of Wilfrid Wilson Gibson.

CONTENTS

JAMES T. FIELDS (1817-1881)

New Hampshire born, Fields came to Boston at sixteen to earn his living. He found work in a combination book store and publishing house. By the time he was twenty-one, he was a junior partner in *Ticknor and Fields*, the foremost publishing firm of his day.

His ground floor office, where he consulted with the greatest of American writers—Emerson, Hawthorne, Lowell, Longfellow, Holmes—has been restored by the city of Boston as a landmark. Today, the walls of the *Old Corner Bookstore* are lined with the famous first editions of the great writers who Fields sponsored.

The Owl-Critic

"Who stuffed that white owl?" No one spoke
    in the shop,
The barber was busy, and he couldn't stop;
The customers, waiting their turns, were
    all reading
The "Daily," the "Herald," the "Post,"
    little heeding
The young man who blurted out such a
    blunt question;
Not one raised a head, or even made a suggestion;
    And the barber kept on shaving.

"Don't you see, Mr. Brown,"
Cried the youth, with a frown,
"How wrong the whole thing is,
How preposterous each wing is,
How flattened the head is, how jammed down
      the neck is—
In short, the whole owl, what an ignorant wreck 't is!
I make no apology;
I've learned owl-eology.
I've passed days and nights in a hundred collections,
And cannot be blinded to any deflections
Arising from unskillful fingers that fail
To stuff a bird right, from his beak to his tail.
Mister Brown! Mister Brown!
Do take that bird down,
Or you'll soon be the laughing-stock all over town!"
    And the barber kept on shaving.

"I've *studied* owls,
And other night-fowls,
And I tell you
What I know to be true;
An owl cannot roost
With his limbs so unloosed;
No owl in this world
Ever had his claws curled,
Ever had his legs slanted,
Ever had his bill canted,
Ever had his neck screwed
Into that attitude.

He can't *do* it, because
'Tis against all bird-laws.
Anatomy teaches,
Ornithology preaches,
An owl has a toe
That *can't* turn out so!
I've made the white owl my study for years,
And to see such a job almost moves me to tears!
Mr. Brown, I'm amazed
You should be so gone crazed
As to put up a bird
In that posture absùrd!
To *look* at that owl really brings on a dizziness
The man who stuffed *him* don't half know
    his business!"
    And the barber kept on shaving.

"Examine those eyes.
I'm filled with surprise
Taxidermists should pass
Off on you such poor glass;
So unnatural they seem
They'd make Audubon scream,
And John Burroughs laugh
To encounter such chaff.
Do take that bird down;
Have him stuffed again, Brown!"
    And the barber kept on shaving.

"With some sawdust and bark
I could stuff in the dark
An owl better than that.
I could make an old hat
Look more like an owl
Than that horrid fowl,
Stuck up there so stiff like a side of coarse leather.
In fact, about *him*, there's not one natural feather."

Just then, with a wink and a sly normal lurch,
The owl, very gravely, got down from his perch,
Walked around, and regarded his fault-finding critic
(Who thought he was stuffed) with a glance analytic,
And then fairly hooted, as if he should say:
"Your learning's at fault *this* time, anyway;
Don't waste it again on a live bird, I pray.
I'm an owl; you're another. Sir Critic, good day!"
          And the barber kept on shaving.

Possibly one of the greatest of all American humorous poems, THE OWL-CRITIC *makes its point with rapier sharpness. The know-it-all youth is humbled not by argument, but by unassailable fact.*

Throughout the poem, there reappears the constant refrain of imperturbability:

          "And the barber kept on shaving."

No need for the barber, who knew what the truth was, to remonstrate—the truth in due time would proclaim itself.

One of the few poets of his day able to earn his living entirely through his pen, Noyes was an avowed traditionalist, his verse very much outside the contemporary mainstream. His verse, stressed on narrative and morals, reflected the literary attitudes of the nineteenth century.

Born and educated in England, Noyes married an American girl and taught at Harvard and Princeton. Later he returned to England and devoted himself entirely to his career as a poet.

The Highwayman

Part One

The wind was a torrent of darkness among the
      gusty trees,
The moon was a ghostly galleon tossed upon
      cloudy seas,
The road was a ribbon of moonlight over the
      purple moor,
And the highwayman came riding—
      Riding—riding—
The highwayman came riding, up to the old inn-door.

He'd a French cocked-hat on his forehead, a bunch
      of lace at his chin,
A coat of the claret velvet, and breeches
      of brown doeskin:

They fitted with never a wrinkle; his boots were
　　　up to the thigh!
And he rode with a jewelled twinkle,
　　　His pistol butts a-twinkle,
His rapier hilt a-twinkle, under the jewelled sky.

Over the cobbles he clattered and clashed in the
　　　dark inn-yard,
And he tapped with his whip on the shutters,
　　　but all was locked and barred:
He whistled a tune to the window, and who should
　　　be waiting there
But the landlord's black-eyed daughter,
　　　Bess, the landlord's daughter,
Plaiting a dark red love-knot into her long black hair.

And dark in the dark old inn-yard a
    stable-wicket creaked
Where Tim, the ostler, listened; his face was white
    and peaked,
His eyes were hollows of madness, his hair
    like moldy hay;
But he loved the landlord's daughter,
        The landlord's red-lipped daughter:
Dumb as a dog he listened, and he heard
    the robber say—

"One kiss, my bonny sweetheart, I'm after
    a prize tonight,
But I shall be back with the yellow gold before
    the morning light.
Yet if they press me sharply, and harry me through
    the day,
Then look for me by moonlight,
        Watch for me by moonlight:
I'll come to thee by moonlight, though Hell should
    bar the way."

He rose upright in the stirrups, he scarce could reach
    her hand;
But she loosened her hair i' the casement! His face
    burnt like a brand
As the black cascade of perfume came tumbling
    over his breast;

And he kissed its waves in the moonlight,
      (Oh, sweet black waves in the moonlight)
Then he tugged at his reins in the moonlight,
      and galloped away to the West.

Part Two

He did not come in the dawning; he did not come
      at noon;
And out of the tawny sunset, before the rise
      o' the moon,
When the road was a gypsy's ribbon, looping
      the purple moor,
A red-coat troop came marching—
      Marching—marching—
King George's men came marching, up to the
      old inn-door.

They said no word to the landlord, they drank
      his ale instead;
But they gagged his daughter and bound her
      to the foot of her narrow bed.
Two of them knelt at her casement, with muskets
      at the side!
There was death at every window;
      And Hell at one dark window;
For Bess could see, through her casement, the road
      that *he* would ride.

They had tied her up to attention, with many
      a sniggering jest:
They had bound a musket beside her, with the barrel
      beneath her breast!
"Now keep good watch!" and they kissed her.
      She heard the dead man say—
Look for me by moonlight;
      Watch for me by moonlight;
I'll come to thee by moonlight, though Hell should
      bar the way!

She twisted her hands behind her; but all the knots
      held good!
She writhed her hands till her fingers were wet
      with sweat or blood!

They stretched and strained in the darkness,
    and the hours crawled by like years;
Till, now, on the stroke of midnight,
      Cold, on the stroke of midnight,
The tip of one finger touched it! The trigger
    at least was hers!

The tip of one finger touched it; she strove no more
    for the rest!
Up, she stood up to attention, with the barrel
    beneath her breast,
She would not risk their hearing: she would not
    strive again;
For the road lay bare in the moonlight,
      Blank and bare in the moonlight;
And the blood of her veins in the moonlight
    throbbed to her Love's refrain.

Tlot-tlot, tlot-tlot! Had they heard it? The horse-hoofs
    ringing clear—
Tlot-tlot, tlot-tlot, in the distance? Were they deaf
    that they did not hear?
Down the ribbon of moonlight, over the brow
    of the hill,
The highwayman came riding,
      Riding, riding!
The red-coats looked to their priming! She stood up
    straight and still!

Tlot-tlot, in the frosty silence; *Tlot-tlot* in the
    echoing night!
Nearer he came and nearer! Her face was like a light!
Her eyes grew wide for a moment; she drew one last
    deep breath,
Then her finger moved in the moonlight,
       Her musket shattered the moonlight,
Shattered her breast in the moonlight and warned him
    —with her death.

He turned; he spurred him Westward; he did not
    know who stood
Bowed with her head o'er the musket, drenched
    with her own red blood!
Not till the dawn he heard it, and slowly blanched
    to hear
How Bess, the landlord's daughter,
       The landlord's black-eyed daughter,
Had watched for her Love in the moonlight;
    and died in the darkness there.

Back, he spurred like a madman, shrieking a curse
    to the sky,
With the white road smoking behind him, and
    his rapier brandished high!
Blood-red were his spurs i' the golden noon;
    wine-red was his velvet coat;

When they shot him down on the highway,
   Down like a dog on the highway,
And he lay in his blood on the highway, with the
   bunch of lace at his throat.

And still a winter's night, they say, when the wind
   is in the trees,
When the moon is a ghostly galleon tossed upon
   cloudy seas,
When the road is a ribbon of moonlight over the
   purple moor,
A highwayman comes riding—
   Riding—riding—
A highwayman comes riding, up to the old inn-door.

Over the cobbles he clatters and clangs in the
   dark inn-yard;
And he taps with his whip on the shutters, but all
   is locked and barred:
He whistles a tune to the window, and who should be
   waiting there
But the landlord's black-eyed daughter,
   Bess, the landlord's daughter,
Plaiting a dark red love-knot into her long black hair.

"The Highwayman" is a poem of high romance abounding with moonlight meetings and tense whisperings. The hero is not a gallant knight, but a highway robber; his sweetheart, no highborn lady, but a common innkeeper's daughter. In this setting, the poet achieves his best effect by casting the rhythm of the poem to imitate the sound of hoofbeats. PART ONE *is all very hushed, the stillness broken only by friendly sounds, the clattering of horses' hoofs, quick tapping at the window, and the whistling of a tune. None of this is very ominous, and the stanzas are filled with sounds appropriate to romance.*

PART TWO *changes sound and tone. Now there is the marching of soldiers, their raucous, sniggering laughter, the cantering of a horse, and the terrible blast of a musket shot. Noise seems to rush in all at once. The vivid descriptions in "The Highwayman" are exceptional. In the first stanza, note the phrase "torrent of darkness"—literally a downpour of blackness; also, the phrases "ghostly galleon" and "ribbon of moonlight." How these three phrases evoke a wild, windy night!*

The poet, like all good balladmakers, repeats stanzas and repeats descriptions. After the climax, the repetition of the early verses, with their same soft, small sounds of courtship, acts on our senses again, but this time the lines bring but ghostlike memories.

WALLACE IRWIN (1875-   )

Associated for many years with the San Francisco Examiner and with Collier's Weekly, Irwin achieved a reputation as a skilled reporter and a humorist of parts.

Blow Me Eyes

When I was young and full o' pride,
    A-standin' on the grass
And gazin' o'er the water-side,
    I seen a fisher lass.
"O, fisher lass, be kind awhile,"
    I asks 'er quite unbid.
"Please look into me face and smile"—
    And, blow me eyes, she did!

      O, blow me light and blow me blow,
        I didn't think she'd charm me so—
          But, blow me eyes, she did!

She seemed so young and beautiful
    I *had* to speak perlite,
(The afternoon was long and dull,
    But she was short and bright).
"This ain't no place," I says, "to stand—
    Let's take a walk instid,
Each holdin' of the other's hand"—
    And, blow me eyes, she did!

O, blow me light and blow me blow,
    I sort o' thunk she wouldn't go—
      But, blow me eyes, she did!

And as we walked along a lane
    With no one else to see,
Me heart was filled with sudden pain,
    And so I says to she:
"If you would have me actions speak
    The words what can't be hid,
You'd sort o' let me kiss yer cheek"—
    And, blow me eyes, she did!

O, blow me light and blow me blow,
    How sweet she was I didn't know—
      But, blow me eyes, *she* did!

But pretty soon me shipmate Jim
  Came strollin' down the beach,
And she began a-oglin' him
  As pretty as a peach.
"O, fickle maid o' false intent,"
  Impulsively I chid,
"Why don't you go and wed that gent?"
  And, blow me eyes, she did!

        O, blow me light and blow me blow,
        I didn't think she'd treat me so—
            But, blow me eyes, she did!

This poem is written as a sea chantey. In almost every sea-men's song, there are constant references to the wind—that element in nature which is the most important to the sailor. The vagaries of the wind and the power of the wind control the life of a sailing-ship. In this ditty, the refrain, emphasiz-ing the word BLOW, *adds special flavor; the expletive,* BLOW ME EYES, *expresses unbounded surprise. And small wonder. For as fickle as the wind is the lass who blows hot and cold.*

The poem has a great lilting rhythm that carries the action forward. The refrain introduces an interesting change in the swing of the lines at just the point where the unexpected happens.

A Nautical Extravaganza

I stood one day by the breezy bay
   A-watchin' the ships go by,
When a tired tar said, with a shake of his head:
   "I wisht I could tell a lie!

"I've saw some sights as would jigger your lights,
   And they've jiggered me own, in sooth,
But I ain't worth a darn at a-spinnin' a yarn
   What wanders away from the truth.

"We was out on the gig, the Riggajig,
   Just a mile and a half to sea,
When Captain Snook, with a troubled look,
   He came and he says to me:

" 'O Bos'n Smith, make haste forthwith
   And hemstitch the for'ard sail;
Accordion pleat the dory sheet,
   For there's going to be a gale.'

"I straightway did as the captain bid—
   No sooner the job was through
When the North wind, whoof; bounced over the roof
   And, murderin' lights—she blew!

27

"She blew the tars right off of the spars,
  And the spars right off of the mast,
And sails and pails and anchors and nails
  Flew by on the wings of the blast.

"Then the galley shook as she blew our cook
  Straight out of the porthole glim,
While pots and pans and kettles and cans
  Went clatterin' after him.

"She blew the fire from our gallant stove
  And the coal from our gallant bin,
She whistled apace past the captain's face
  And blew the beard off his chin!

" 'O wizzle me dead!' the captain said
  (And the words blew out of his mouth);
'We're lost, I fear, if the wind don't veer
  And blow awhile from the south.'

"And wizzle me dead! No sooner he'd said
   Them words that blew out from his mouth,
Than the wind switched round with a
       hurricane sound
   And blew straight in from the south.

"And we opened our eyes with a wild surprise,
   And never a word to say—
In changin' her tack the wind blew back
   The things that she'd blew away!

"She blew the tars back onto the spars,
   And the spars back onto the mast;
Back flew the pails and the sails and the nails,
   Which into the ship stuck fast.

"And 'fore we could look she blew the cook
  Straight into the galley coop,
Back dropped the pans and kettles and cans,
  Without even spillin' the soup.

"She blew the fire back into the stove
  Where it burned in its proper place—
And all of us cheered as she blew the beard
  Back onto the captain's face.

"There's more of my tale,"
  Said the sailor hale,
    "As would jigger your lights, in sooth;
But I ain't worth a darn
  At a-spinnin' a yarn
    What wanders away from the truth."

*Here is indeed a jolly chantey. The title is particularly well
chosen, for imagination runs riot.*
  *The middle rhyme is employed in most of the first and
third sentences of each quatrain, and these middle rhymes
impart great charm and quicken the rhythm enormously.*

SIR WALTER SCOTT (1771-1832)

Scotland's famous poet, novelist, and historian grew up under the care of his grandfather, a shepherd who filled him with ancient tales.

Scott's fondness for the old ballads of wild adventure colored all his writings. His collection of songs of the Scottish Border set the pattern for his romantic poetry.

Scott's long series of Waverly novels changed the course of English fiction; he popularized romantic adventure in an historically accurate setting.

Lochinvar

Oh, young Lochinvar is come out of the West,—
Through all the wide Border his steed was the best,
And save his good broadsword he weapons had none,—
He rode all unarm'd and he rode all alone.
So faithful in love, and so dauntless in war,
There never was knight like the young Lochinvar.

He stay'd not for brake, and he stopp'd not for stone,
He swam the Eske river where ford there was none,
But ere he alighted at Netherby gate,
The bride had consented, the gallant came late;
For a laggard in love and a dastard in war
Was to wed the fair Ellen of brave Lochinvar.

So boldly he enter'd the Netherby hall,
'Mong bridesmen and kinsmen and brothers and all.
Then spoke the bride's father, his hand on his sword
(For the poor craven bridegroom said never a word),
"Oh, come ye in peace here, or come ye in war,
Or to dance at our bridal, young Lord Lochinvar?"

"I long woo'd your daughter,—my suit you denied;
Love swells like the Solway, but ebbs like its tide;
And now am I come, with this lost love of mine
To lead but one measure, drink one cup of wine.
There are maidens in Scotland more lovely, by far,
That would gladly be bride to the young Lochinvar."

The bride kissed the goblet, the knight took it up,
He quaff'd off the wine and he threw down the cup.
She look'd down to blush, and she look'd up to sigh,
With a smile on her lips and a tear in her eye.
He took her soft hand ere her mother could bar:
"Now tread we a measure," said young Lochinvar.

So stately his form, and so lovely her face,
That never a hall such a galliard did grace,
While her mother did fret, and her father did fume,
And the bridegroom stood dangling his bonnet
        and plume,
And the bridesmaidens whisper'd, " 'Twere better
        by far
To have match'd our fair cousin with young
        Lochinvar."

One touch to her hand, and one word in her ear,
When they reach'd the hall-door, and the charger
        stood near;
So light to the croupe the fair lady he swung,
So light to the saddle before her he sprung!

"She is won! we are gone, over bank, bush, and scaur;
They'll have fleet steeds that follow,"
      quoth young Lochinvar.

There was mounting 'mong Græmes of the
      Netherby clan;
Forsters, Fenwicks, and Musgraves, they rode and
      they ran;
There was racing and chasing on Cannobie Lee,
But the lost bride of Netherby ne'er did they see.
So daring in love, and so dauntless in war,
Have ye e'er heard of gallant like young Lochinvar?

*The poet describes the appearance and manner of young
Lochinvar in so heroic a way that the reader is eager that
he somehow win back the bride, even though she is in the
midst of her wedding party. To ensure that we admire
Lochinvar, the jilted bridegroom is presented as a despic-
able, foolish milksop.*

    *The stern old father is afraid of Lochinvar. "Do you
come in peace or war?" he asks.*

    *Lochinvar is clever. He is alone among strangers.
There are probably 50 or more people in Netherby Hall,
ready to support their old chief, should the interloper reply
in anger. But he is not sure that Ellen still prefers to be his
wife. To gain time, to discover her true feelings, and to
allay suspicion, he answers, "I have come to drink and to
dance." But at the same time he boastfully adds:*

"There are maidens in Scotland more lovely, by far,
  That would gladly be bride to the young Lochinvar."

At medieval festivities, a special mark of hospitality to
an honored guest was the offering of wine by the female
head of the household. When Ellen not only takes this duty
upon herself, but kisses the goblet before handing it to
Lochinvar, he has his answer.

It was a sign of wealth to be able to afford a new glass
for each drink; it was also a sign of the recognition of this
wealth by the guest if he, too, broke his wineglass. When
Lochinvar throws down the cup, he is pretending to be
respectful of the Netherby clan. At the same time, he is
plotting an elopement that will bring them all chasing at
his heels.

Just as the King, earlier, had been worried, now the
Queen is becoming upset. But everyone else is filled with
admiration for the lovely young couple dancing together.
The bridesmaids are enchanted; they whisper that surely
the choice should have been the handsome Lochinvar. All
the young women are on the side of the stranger; the men
will have to be outrun or outfought. At just the right moment, Lochinvar waltzes Ellen right out the door, swings
her up on to his horse, and rides off.

Glance back to the beginning of the poem, at the description of Lochinvar's ability as a horseman. Here we
have a good example of how descriptive details become
important to a story. The man who could keep his horse
steady coming across the river on bramble fields (brake)
and on unsmooth roads (stone) can easily outride all the
Forsters, the Fenwicks, and the Musgraves, as he gallops
back over bank, brake, and scauer (protruding stones).
Even the rhythm of the verses are like that cantering horse
and his gallant rider.

Born in Albany, New York, the son of a schoolteacher, Harte started work when he was thirteen as a clerk in a lawyer's office. Then he became a clerk in a bank, then an express messenger on a dangerous mountain route. Later, he taught school, clerked in a drug store, and did some prospecting.

He found his career after he joined a newspaper staff where for a dollar a column, he wrote stories to fill space, stories that today are reprinted in every anthology of American literature.

But perhaps he is just as well known for his sly, comic poems about picturesque Western characters.

The Society upon the Stanislaus

I reside at Table Mountain, and my name is
   Truthful James;
I am not up to small deceit, or any sinful games;
And I'll tell in simple language what I know
   about the row
That broke up our society upon the Stanislow.

But first I would remark that it is not a proper plan
For any scientific man to whale his fellow man,
And if a member don't agree with his peculiar whim,
To lay for that same member, so to razzle-dazzle him.

Now, nothing could be finer or more beautiful to see
Than the first six months' proceedings of that
   same society;
Till Brown of Calaveras brought a lot of fossil bones
That he found within a tunnel near the
   residence of Jones.

Then Brown he read a paper, and he
   reconstructed there,
From those same bones, an animal that was
   extremely rare;
And Jones then asked the Chair for a suspension
   of the rules,
Till he could prove that those same bones was
   one of his lost mules.

Then Brown, he smiled a bitter smile, and said
   he was at fault,
It seemed he had been trespassing on Jones's
   family vault;
He was a most sarcastic man, this quiet Mr. Brown;
He had the kind of acrid smile that almost
   was a frown.

Now, I hold it is not decent for a scientific gent
To say another is an ass—at least, to all intent;
Nor should the individual who happens to be meant
Reply by heaving rocks at him to any great extent.

Then Abner Dean of Angel's raised a point
     of order, when
A chunk of old red sandstone took him in
     the abdomen;
And he smiled a kind of sickly smile, and curled
     up on the floor,
And the subsequent proceedings interested him
     no more.

For in less time than I write it, every member
     did engage
In a warfare with the remnants of a palaeozoic age;
And the way they heaved those fossils in their
     anger was a sin,
Till the skull of an old mammoth caved the head
     of Thompson in.

And this is all I have to say of these improper games
For I live at Table Mountain, and my name is
　　　Truthful James;
And I've told, in simple language, what I know
　　　about the row
That broke up our society upon the Stanislow.

*An outstanding piece of American humor! The author is
making fun of the pseudo-scientific fraternity, and is chid-
ing the human foible of taking umbrage when anyone dares
to question the validity of one's beliefs. The pretenders who
would have you believe that they are genuine scholars
quickly lose all objectivity, and the learned members wind
up by heaving rocks at each other. When one's ideas are
questioned, nothing is sacred, and science and perspective
vanish.*

JOHN HENRY TITUS (1853-1947)

In 1934, John Henry Titus brought a legal action against Hugh Antoine D'Arcy, an actor who had been reciting *The Face on the Barroom Floor* as part of his repertoire, while alleging that the poem was original with him. The results of the lawsuit did not clearly establish the authorship.

It was not even certain when the poem first appeared in print. Some claim that the ballad was first published in the Ashtabula (Ohio) Sentinel in 1872; others that it first appeared in the New York Dispatch of 1887.

The Face on the Barroom Floor

'Twas a balmy summer evening, and a goodly crowd
    was there,
Which well-nigh filled Joe's barroom on the
    corner of the square,
And as songs and witty stories came through the
    open door
A vagabond crept slowly in and posed upon
    the floor.

"Where did it come from?" someone said:
    "The wind has blown it in."
"What does it want?" another cried. "Some whisky,
    rum or gin?"

"Here, Toby, seek him, if your stomach's equal
  to the work—
I wouldn't touch him with a fork, he's as filthy
  as a Turk."

This badinage the poor wretch took with stoical
  good grace;
In fact, he smiled as though he thought he'd struck
  the proper place.
"Come, boys, I know there's kindly hearts among
  so good a crowd—
To be in such good company would make
  a deacon proud.

41

"Give me a drink—that's what I want—I'm out of
            funds, you know;
When I had cash to treat the gang, this hand
            was never slow.
What? You laugh as though you thought this pocket
            never held a sou;
I once was fixed as well, my boys, as anyone
            of you.

"There, thanks; that's braced me nicely; God bless
            you one and all;
Next time I pass this good saloon, I'll make
            another call.
Give you a song? No, I can't do that, my singing
            days are past;
My voice is cracked, my throat's worn out,
            and my lungs are going fast.

"Say! Give me another whisky, and I'll tell you
            what I'll do—
I'll tell you a funny story, and a fact,
            I promise, too.

That I was ever a decent man not one of you
            would think;
But I was, some four or five years back. Say,
            give me another drink.

"Fill her up, Joe, I want to put some lift into
      my frame—
Such little drinks, to a bum like me,
      are miserably tame;
Five fingers—there, that's the scheme—and
      corking whisky, too.
Well, here's luck, boys; and, landlord, my best
      regards to you.

"You've treated me pretty kindly, and I'd like to
      tell you how
I came to be the dirty sot you see before
      you now.
As I told you, once I was a man, with muscle,
      frame and health,
And, but for a blunder, ought to have made
      considerable wealth.

"I was a painter—not one that daubed on
      bricks and wood
But an artist, and, for my age, was rated
      pretty good.
I worked hard at my canvas and was bidding
      fair to rise,
For gradually I saw the star of fame
      before my eyes.

"I made a picture, perhaps you've seen, 'tis called
    the 'Chase of Fame.'
It brought me a thousand dollars and added
    to my name.
And then I met a woman—now comes the
    funny part—
With eyes that petrified my brain, and sank
    into my heart.

"Why don't you laugh? 'Tis funny that the
    vagabond you see
Could ever love a woman and expect her
    love for me;
But for two blessed months and more her smiles
    were freely given,
And when her loving lips touched mine it
    carried me to heaven.

"Say, boys, did you ever see a woman for whom
    your soul you'd give,
With a form like the Milo Venus, too
    beautiful to live;
With eyes that would beat the Koh-i-noor, and a
    wealth of chestnut hair?
If so, 'twas she, for no one else was ever half
    so fair.

"I was working on a portrait, one afternoon
          in May,
Of a fair-haired boy, a friend of mine, who lived
          across the way,
And Madeline admired it, and much to
          my surprise,
Said she'd like to know the man that had
          such dreamy eyes.

"It didn't take long to know him, and before the
          month had flown
My friend had stole' my darling, and I was
          left alone;
And, ere a year of misery had passed above
          my head,
This aching, breaking heart of mine had withered
          and was dead.

"That's why I took to drink, boys. Why, I never
          saw you smile,
I thought you'd be amused, and laughing all
          the while.
Why, what's the matter, friend? There's a teardrop
          in your eye,
Come, laugh, like me; 'tis women that
          should cry.

"Say, boys, give me another whisky, and that will
       make me glad,
And I'll draw right here a picture of the face
       that drove me mad.
Hand me, please, that chalk with which you mark
       the baseball score—
You'll see the lovely Madeline upon this
       barroom floor."

Another drink, and with chalk in hand the
       vagabond began
To sketch a face that well might buy the
       soul of any man.
Then, as he placed another lock upon the
       shapely head,
With fearful shriek, he leaped and fell across
       the picture—dead.

*In the early 1900's, this poem was the darling of elocution
teachers and the tour de force of many a vaudeville actor.
Today, we regard this production as a corny tearjerker.
Nevertheless, parts of the poem are quite moving.*

A native of Scotland, Service emigrated to the Yukon where he worked for eight years as an employee of the Canadian Bank of Commerce. Later, he was sent to Europe by a Toronto newspaper to report on the Balkan War. He found France very much to his taste and remained there.

During World War I, he volunteered to serve in the ambulance corps. In 1939, he was caught in Warsaw by the outbreak of hostilities and barely escaped the bombardment of that city; and when the German army invaded French soil during World War II, he again was forced to make a desperate flight to safe territory.

It was 1940 when he entered the United States. He spent a brief period in Hollywood where he observed the filming of his adventurous life. Then he went back once again to France, there to spend his final years.

The Cremation of Sam McGee

There are strange things done in the midnight sun
  By the men who moil for gold;
The Arctic trails have their secret tales
  That would make your blood run cold;
The Northern Lights have seen queer sights,
  But the queerest they ever did see
Was that night on the marge of Lake Lebarge
  I cremated Sam McGee.

Now Sam McGee was from Tennessee,
    where the cotton blooms and blows.
Why he left his home in the South to roam
    'round the Pole, God only knows.
He was always cold, but the land of gold seemed
    to hold him like a spell;
Though he'd often say in his homely way that
    "he'd sooner live in hell."

On a Christmas Day we were mushing our way
    over the Dawson trail.
Talk of your cold! through the parka's fold it stabbed
    like a driven nail.
If our eyes we'd close, then the lashes froze
    till sometimes we couldn't see;
It wasn't much fun, but the only one to whimper
    was Sam McGee.

And that very night, as we lay packed tight
        in our robes beneath the snow,
And the dogs were fed, and the stars o'erhead
        were dancing heel and toe,
He turned to me, and "Cap," says he, "I'll cash in
        this trip, I guess;
And if I do, I'm asking that you won't refuse
        my last request."

Well, he seemed so low that I couldn't say no;
        then he says with a sort of moan:
"It's the cursèd cold, and it's got right hold till I'm
        chilled clean through to the bone.
Yet 'tain't being dead—it's my awful dread of the
        icy grave that pains;
So I want you to swear that, foul or fair, you'll
        cremate my last remains."

A pal's last need is a thing to heed, so I swore
        I would not fail;
And we started on at the streak of dawn; but God!
        he looked ghastly pale.
He crouched on the sleigh, and he raved all day
        of his home in Tennessee;
And before nightfall a corpse was all that was left
        of Sam McGee.

There wasn't a breath in that land of death, and I
      hurried, horror-driven,
With a corpse half hid that I couldn't get rid,
      because of a promise given;
It was lashed to the sleigh, and it seemed to say:
      "You may tax your brawn and brains,
But you promised true, and it's up to you to cremate
      those last remains."

Now a promise made is a debt unpaid, and the trail
      has its own stern code.
In the days to come, though my lips were dumb,
      in my heart how I cursed that load.
In the long, long night, by the lone firelight,
      while the huskies, round in a ring,
Howled out their woes to the homeless snows—
      O God! how I loathed the thing.

And every day that quiet clay seemed to heavy
      and heavier grow;
And on I went, though the dogs were spent and the
      grub was getting low;
The trail was bad, and I felt half mad, but I swore
      I would not give in;
And I'd often sing to the hateful thing, and it
      harkened with a grin.

Till I came to the marge of Lake Lebarge, and a
    derelict there lay;
It was jammed in the ice, but I saw in a trice
    it was called the "Alice May."
And I looked at it, and I thought a bit, and I looked
    at my frozen chum;
Then "Here," said I, with a sudden cry,
    "is my cre-ma-tor-eum."

Some planks I tore from the cabin floor, and I lit
    the boiler fire;
Some coal I found that was lying around,
    and I heaped the fuel higher;
The flames just soared, and the furnace roared—such
    a blaze you seldom see;
And I burrowed a hole in the glowing coal, and
    I stuffed in Sam McGee.

Then I made a hike, for I didn't like to hear
    him sizzle so;
And the heavens scowled, and the huskies howled,
    and the wind began to blow.
It was icy cold, but the hot sweat rolled down my
    cheeks, and I don't know why;
And the greasy smoke in an inky cloak went
    streaking down the sky.

I do not know how long in the snow I wrestled
    with grisly fear;
But the stars came out and they danced about
    ere again I ventured near;
I was sick with dread, but I bravely said:
    "I'll just take a peep inside.
I guess he's cooked, and it's time I looked;"
    . . . then the door I opened wide.

And there sat Sam, looking cool and calm,
    in the heart of the furnace roar;
And he wore a smile you could see a mile, and he
    said: "Please close that door.
It's fine in here, but I greatly fear you'll let in
    the cold and storm!
Since I left Plumtree, down in Tennessee, it's the first
    time I've been warm."

There are strange things done in the midnight sun
   By the men who moil for gold;
The Arctic trails have their secret tales
   That would make your blood run cold;
The Northern Lights have seen queer sights,
   But the queerest they ever did see
Was that night on the marge of Lake Lebarge
   I cremated Sam McGee.

In light verse of this kind, we get so engrossed with the fantasy and the humor we are likely to overlook the fine imagery. The description "and the stars o'erhead were dancing heel and toe," is a memorable line.

    Notice, too, how Service effectively employs the middle rhyme in most of his lines.

Jean Desprez

Oh, ye whose hearts are resonant, and ring
    to War's romance,
Hear ye the story of a boy, a peasant boy of France;
A lad uncouth and warped with toil, yet who,
    when trial came,
Could feel within his soul upleap and soar
    the sacred flame;
Could stand upright, and scorn and smite,
    as only heroes may:
Oh, hearken! Let me try to tell the tale
    of Jean Desprez.

With fire and sword the Teuton horde was ravaging
    the land,
And there was darkness and despair, grim death
    on every hand;
Red fields of slaughter sloping down to ruin's
    black abyss;
The wolves of war ran evil-fanged, and little
    did they miss.
And on they came with fear and flame, to burn
    and loot and slay,
Until they reached the red-roofed croft, the home
    of Jean Desprez.

"Rout out the village, one and all!" the Uhlan
    Captain said.
"Behold! Some hand has fired a shot. My trumpeteer
    is dead.
Now shall they Prussian vengeance know; now shall
    they rue the day,
For by this sacred German slain, ten of these dogs
    shall pay."

They drove the cowering peasants forth, women
    and babies and men,
And from the last, with many a jeer, the Captain
    chose he ten;
Ten simple peasants, bowed with toil; they stood, they
    knew not why,
Against the grey wall of the church, hearing their
    children cry;
Hearing their wives and mothers wail, with faces
    dazed they stood.
A moment only . . . *Ready! Fire!* They weltered in
    their blood.

But there was one who gazed unseen, who heard the
    frenzied cries,
Who saw these men in sabots fall before their
    children's eyes;
A Zouave wounded in a ditch, and knowing death
    was nigh,

He laughed with joy: "Ah! here is where I settle
ere I die."
He clutched his rifle once again, and long he
aimed and well. . . .
A shot! Beside his victims ten the Uhlan Captain fell.

They dragged the wounded Zouave out; their rage
was like a flame.
With bayonets they pinned him down, until their
Major came.
A blond, full-blooded man he was, and arrogant
of eye;
He stared to see with shattered skull his favorite
Captain lie.

"Nay, do not finish him so quick, this foreign swine,"
    he cried;
"Go nail him to the big church door; he shall
    be crucified."
With bayonets through hands and feet they nailed
    the Zouave there,
And there was anguish in his eyes, and horror
    in his stare;

"Water! A single drop!" he moaned; but how they
        jeered at him,
And mocked him with an empty cup, and saw his
        sight grow dim;
And as in agony of death with blood his lips were wet,
The Prussian Major gaily laughed, and lit a cigarette.

But mid the white-faced villagers who cowered
        in horror by,
Was one who saw the woeful sight, who heard
        the woeful cry:
"Water! One little drop, I beg! For love of Christ
        who died. . . ."
It was the little Jean Desprez who turned
        and stole aside;
It was the little bare-foot boy who came
        with cup abrim
And walked up to the dying man, and gave the
        drink to him.

A roar of rage! They seize the boy; they tear him
        fast away.
The Prussian Major swings around; no longer
        is he gay.
His teeth are wolfishly agleam; his face all dark
        with spite:
"Go, shoot the brat," he snarls, "that dare defy our
        Prussian might.

Yet stay! I have another thought. I'll kindly be,
    and spare;
Quick; give the lad a rifle charged, and set him
    squarely there,
And bid him shoot, and shoot to kill. Haste! Make
    him understand
The dying dog he fain would save shall perish
    by his hand.
And all his kindred they shall see, and all shall
    curse his name,
Who bought his life at such a cost, the price of
    death and shame."

They brought the boy, wild-eyed with fear; they
    made him understand;
They stood him by the dying man, a rifle in his hand.
"Make haste!" said they; "the time is short, and you
    must kill or die."
The Major puffed his cigarette, amusement in his eye.
And then the dying Zouave heard, and raised his
    weary head:
"Shoot, son, 'twill be the best for both; shoot swift
    and straight," he said.
"Fire first and last, and do not flinch; for lost
    to hope am I;
And I will murmur: *Vive La France!* and bless you
    ere I die."

Half-blind with blows the boy stood there; he
    seemed to swoon and sway;
Then in that moment woke the soul of little
    Jean Desprez.
He saw the woods go sheening down; the larks
    were singing clear;
And oh! the scents and sounds of spring, how sweet
    they were! how dear!
He felt the scent of new-mown hay, a soft breeze
    fanned his brow;
O God! the paths of peace and toil! How precious
    were they now!
The summer days and summer ways, how bright
    with hope and bliss!
The autumn such a dream of gold . . . and all must
    end in this:
This shining rifle in his hand, that shambles
    all around;
The Zouave there with dying glare; the blood upon
    the ground;
The brutal faces round him ringed, the evil
    eyes aflame;
That Prussian bully standing by, as if he watched
    a game.
"Make haste and shoot," the Major sneered;
    "a minute more I give;
A minute more to kill your friend, if you yourself
    would live."

They only saw a bare-foot boy, with blanched
    and twitching face;
They did not see within his eyes the glory of his race;
The glory of a million men who for fair France
    have died,
The splendor of self-sacrifice that will not be denied.
Yet . . . he was but a peasant lad, and oh! but life
    was sweet. . . .
"Your minute's nearly gone, my lad," he heard
    a voice repeat.
"Shoot! Shoot!" the dying Zouave moaned; "Shoot!
    Shoot!" the soldiers said.
Then Jean Desprez reached out and shot . . .
    the Prussian Major dead!

The rhythm of this poem is so marked that it is very easy to get caught up in it and misread the lines. This is especially true of the last two lines of the poem where almost without thinking, one accents the second "Shoot" in each part of the line.

    This is probably Robert Service's greatest melodrama. The poet leads the reader on unerringly to the final climax. No matter how sentimental the story, we are nevertheless moved by the climax.

WILLIAM ROBERT SPENCER (1769-1834)

A popular and witty host in British society, Spencer was called "The Perfect Aristocrat" by Lord Byron. His poems, always polished and deft, deal with matters of interest to the aristocratic society of his day.

Beth-Gelert

The spearmen heard the bugle sound,
    And cheerily smiled the morn;
And many a brach, and many a hound
    Obeyed Llewellyn's horn.

And still he blew a louder blast,
    And gave a lustier cheer,
"Come, Gêlert, come, wert never last
    Llewellyn's horn to hear.

"O where does faithful Gêlert roam
    The flower of all his race;
So true, so brave—a lamb at home,
    A lion in the chase?"

In sooth, he was a peerless hound,
    The gift of royal John;
But now no Gêlert could be found,
    And all the chase rode on.

That day Llewellyn little loved
   The chase of hart and hare;
And scant and small the booty proved,
   For Gêlert was not there.

Unpleased, Llewellyn homeward hied,
   When, near the portal seat,
His truant Gêlert he espied
   Bounding his lord to greet.

But when he gained the castle-door,
   Aghast the chieftain stood;
The hound all o'er was smeared with gore;
   His lips, his fangs, ran blood.

Llewellyn gazed with fierce surprise;
   Unused such looks to meet,
His favorite checked his joyful guise,
   And crouched, and licked his feet.

Onward, in haste, Llewelyn passed,
   And on went Gêlert too;
And still, where'er his eyes he cast,
   Fresh blood-gouts shocked his view.

O'erturned his infant's bed he found,
   With blood-stained covert rent;
And all around the walls and ground
   With recent blood besprent.

He called his child—no voice replied—
　　He searched with terror wild;
Blood, blood he found on every side,
　　But nowhere found his child.

"Hell-hound! my child's by thee devoured,"
　　The frantic father cried;
And to the hilt his vengeful sword
　　He plunged in Gêlert's side.

Aroused by Gêlert's dying yell,
　　Some slumberer wakened nigh;
What words the parent's joy could tell
　　To hear his infant's cry!

Concealed beneath a tumbled heap
   His hurried search had missed,
All glowing from his rosy sleep
   The cherub boy he kissed.

Nor scathe had he, nor harm, nor dread,
   But, the same couch beneath,
Lay a gaunt wolf, all torn and dead,
   Tremendous still in death.

Ah, what was then Llewellyn's pain!
For now the truth was clear;
His gallant hound the wolf had slain
To save Llewellyn's heir.

As the poem opens, Llewellyn is calling to his dogs and to his men to gather for the hunt. His favorite dog, Beth-Gelert, does not answer his bugle call. Impatiently, Llewellyn rides off. The merry chase is a disappointment, and the hunter wends his way home without booty.

He is greeted by Beth-Gelert who is wounded and bloody. Llewellyn gazes at his injured hound—not with sympathy, but with "fierce surprise." He hurries from room to room, finding everywhere marks of disaster. To his horror, he discovers his infant's cradle overturned, and the boy nowhere in sight. The hot-headed lord assumes the hound has devoured his son. In unthinking rage, he stabs Beth-Gelert to death. Seconds later the boy is discovered safe and sound under a couch. By his side lies a mangled wolf, slain by Beth-Gelert "to save Llewellyn's heir." What pain Llewellyn now suffers for the useless slaying of his gallant hound!

This ballad is one of the best known English rhymed folk tales. Its name was intended to give a clue to the nature of the dog it celebrates, for in old Saxon, Beth-Gelert means "brightest among the smartest."

Although he never attended school, this Englishman has
published over 30 volumes of poetry. His interests focus
entirely on the fate of the common man and on the grim
melodramas of common experience.

The Stone

"And you will cut a stone for him,
To set above his head?
And will you cut a stone for him—
A stone for him?" she said.

Three days before, a splintered rock
Had struck her lover dead—
Had struck him in the quarry dead,
Where, careless of the warning call,
He loitered, while the shot was fired—
A lively stripling, brave and tall,
And sure of all his heart desired . . .
A flash, a shock,
A rumbling fall . . .
And, broken 'neath the broken rock,
A lifeless heap, with face of clay;
And still as any stone he lay,
With eyes that saw the end of all.

I went to break the news to her;
And I could hear my own heart beat
With dread of what my lips might say
But, some poor fool had sped before;
And flinging wide her father's door,
Had blurted out the news to her,
Had struck her lover dead for her,
Had struck the girl's heart dead in her,
Had struck life lifeless at a word,
And dropped it at her feet:
Then hurried on his witless way,
Scarce knowing she had heard.

And when I came, she stood alone,
A woman turned to stone:
And, though no word at all she said,
I knew that all was known.
Because her heart was dead,
She did not sigh nor moan,
His mother wept;
She could not weep.
Her lover slept:
She could not sleep.
Three days, three nights,
She did not stir:
Three days, three nights,
Were one to her,
Who never closed her eyes

From sunset to sunrise,
From dawn to evenfall:
Her tearless, staring eyes,
That seeing naught, saw all.

The fourth night when I came from work,
I found her at my door.
"And will you cut a stone for him?"
She said: and spoke no more:
But followed me, as I went in,
And sank upon a chair;
And fixed her gray eyes on my face,
With still, unseeing stare.
And, as she waited patiently,
I could not bear to feel
Those still, gray eyes that followed me,
Those eyes that plucked the heart from me,
Those eyes that sucked the breath from me
And curdled the warm blood in me,
Those eyes that cut me to the bone,
And pierced my marrow like cold steel.

And so I rose, and sought a stone;
And cut it, smooth and square:
And, as I worked, she sat and watched,
Beside me, in her chair.
Night after night, by candlelight,
I cut her lover's name:

Night after night, so still and white,
And like a ghost she came;
And sat beside me in her chair;
And watched with eyes aflame.
She eyed each stroke;
And hardly stirred:
She never spoke
A single word:
And not a sound or murmur broke
The quiet, save the mallet-stroke.
With still eyes ever on my hands,
With eyes that seemed to burn my hands,
My wincing, overwearied hands,

She watched, with bloodless lips apart,
And silent, indrawn breath:
And every stroke my chisel cut,
Death cut still deeper in her heart:
The two of us were chiseling,
Together, I and death.

And when at length the job was done,
And I had laid the mallet by,
As if, at last, her peace were won,
She breathed his name; and, with a sigh,

Passed slowly through the open door:
And never crossed my threshold more.

Next night I labored late, alone.
To cut her name upon the stone.

How carefully the poet has prepared us for the fate of the grieving maiden. Using the device of flashback, Gibson is able to tell us what has happened: not only has there been an accidental death, but a young girl has been told of it so suddenly, she has experienced a fatal shock. The news came to the one as unexpectedly as death came to the other, and both boy and girl have been turned to stone.

Throughout the entire ballad, all the words follow the lead of that keyword STONE. *They are all short words with a hollow clipped sound, and the words seem to fall upon our ears like the short strokes of the stonemason's hammer, as he taps out the name of the young man. Like the inexorable hand of fate, the stonecutter chisels out the story of doom.*

The poet gracefully returns us to the story by having the girl repeat her request for the tombstone. Now we realize that all her life processes have stopped; she has neither eaten nor slept for three days; her broken heart has dropped down lifeless; her eyes are tearless and staring; she grows more and more still and white, she becomes "like a ghost," never stirs, never speaks; her lips are bloodless.

The only contrast between the lost young man and the nearly lifeless girl is time. The lover "so sure of all his heart desired" fell swiftly and suddenly; the young girl, grieving so desperately, met death slowly — but inevitably.

HERBERT KAUFMAN (1878-1947)

As an American journalist, he wrote syndicated news columns commenting on international events. During World War I, he was actively engaged in publicizing the Federal Food Commission, the American organization that prevented the starvation of millions.

The Hell Gate of Soissons is the only one of his poems that has achieved fame.

The Hell – Gate of Soissons

My name is Darino, the poet. You have heard?
    Oui, Comédie Française.
Perchance it has happened, *mon ami,* you know
    of my unworthy lays.
Ah, then you must guess how my fingers are itching
    to talk to a pen;
For I was at Soissons, and saw it, the death of the
    twelve Englishmen.

My leg, *malheureusement,* I left it behind on the
    banks of the Aisne.
Regret? I would pay with the other to witness
    their valor again.
A trifle, indeed, I assure you, to give for
    the honor to tell
How that handful of British, undaunted, went into
    the Gateway of Hell.

Let me draw you a plan of the battle. Here we French
    and your Engineers stood;
Over there a detachment of German sharpshooters
    lay hid in a wood.
A *mitrailleuse* battery planted on top of this
    well-chosen ridge
Held the road for the Prussians and covered
    the direct approach to the bridge.

It was madness to dare the dense murder that
    spewed from those ghastly machines.
(Only those who have danced to its music can know
    what the *mitrailleuse* means.)

But the bridge on the Aisne was a menace; our safety
    demanded its fall:
"Engineers—volunteers!" In a body, the Royals
    stood out at the call.

Death at best was the fate of that mission—to
    their glory not one was dismayed.
A party was chosen—and seven survived till
    the powder was laid.
And *they* died with their fuses unlighted. Another
    detachment! Again
A sortie is made—all too vainly. The bridge still
    commanded the Aisne.

We were fighting two foes—Time and Prussia—
    the moments were worth more than troops.
We *must* blow up the bridge. A lone soldier darts out
    from the Royals and swoops
For the fuse! Fate seems with us. We cheer him;
    he answers—our hopes are reborn!
A ball rips his visor—his khaki shows red where
    another has torn.

Will he live—will he last—will he make it? *Hélas!*
    And so near to the goal!
A second, he dies! then a third one! A fourth!
    Still the Germans take toll!
A fifth, *magnifique!* It is magic! How does he
    escape them? He may . . .
Yes, he *does!* See, the match flares! A rifle rings out
    from the wood and says "Nay!"

Six, seven, eight, nine take their places; six, seven,
    eight, nine brave their hail:
Six, seven, eight, nine—how we count them! But the
    sixth, seventh, eighth, and ninth fail!
A tenth! *Sacré nom!* But these English are soldiers—
    they know how to try;
(He fumbles the place where his jaw was)—they
    show, too, how heroes can die.

Ten we count—ten who ventured unquailing—
    ten there were—and ten are no more!

Yet another salutes and superbly essays where
  the ten failed before.
God of Battles, look down and protect him! Lord,
  his heart is as Thine—let him live!
But the *mitrailleuse* splutters and stutters, and riddles
  him into a sieve.

Then I thought of my sins, and sat waiting the charge
  that we could not withstand.
And I thought of my beautiful Paris, and gave a last
  look at the land,
At France, my *belle France*, in her glory of blue sky
  and green field and wood.
Death with honor, but never surrender. And to die
  with such men—it was good.

They are forming—the bugles are blaring—they will
  cross in a moment and then—
When out of the line of the Royals (your island,
  mon ami, breeds men)
Bursts a private, a tawny-haired giant—it was
  hopeless, but *ciel?* how he ran!
Bon Dieu please remember the pattern, and make
  many more on his plan!

No cheers from our ranks, and the Germans, they
  halted in wonderment, too;
See, he reaches the bridge; ah! he lights it! I am
  dreaming, it *cannot* be true.

Screams of rage! *Fusillade!* They have killed him!
    Too late though, the good work is done.
By the valor of twelve English martyrs, the Hell-Gate
    of Soissons is won!

*During World War I, this poem was a favorite of the elocu-
tion class and the high school auditorium. There is far more
drama in the recitation of these verses than there is in the
reading of them. The lines are loaded with action, with
suspense, and at moments, with pathos. The nobility of Man
in facing overwhelming odds comes through inspiringly.*

HENRY WADSWORTH LONGFELLOW (1807-1882)

Born in Portland, Maine, the son of a prosperous lawyer, Longfellow was surrounded with good music and poetry. He read widely in the splendid library of his home.

He prepared himself for a career as a teacher of modern languages. He traveled widely, acquiring facility in seven European tongues. For 17 years, he served as professor of languages and literature at Harvard.

He then retired to devote himself entirely to poetry. His translations of foreign poems fill 31 volumes.

The Wreck of the Hesperus

It was the schooner Hesperus,
    That sailed the wintry sea;
And the skipper had taken his little daughter,
    To bear him company.

Blue were her eyes as the fairy-flax,
    Her cheeks like the dawn of day,
And her bosom white as the hawthorn buds
    That ope in the month of May.

The skipper he stood beside the helm,
    His pipe was in his mouth,
And he watched how the veering flaw did blow
    The smoke now West, now South.

Then up and spake an old sailor,
  Had sailed the Spanish Main,
"I pray thee, put into yonder port,
  For I fear a hurricane.

"Last night, the moon had a golden ring,
  And to-night no moon we see!"
The skipper, he blew a whiff from his pipe,
  And a scornful laugh laughed he.

Colder and louder blew the wind,
    A gale from the Northeast,
The snow fell hissing in the brine,
    And the billows frothed like yeast.

Down came the storm, and smote amain
    The vessel in its strength;
She shuddered and paused, like a frightened steed,
    Then leaped her cable's length.

"Come hither! come hither! my little daughter,
    And do not tremble so;
For I can weather the roughest gale
    That ever wind did blow."

He wrapped her warm in his seaman's coat
   Against the stinging blast;
He cut a rope from a broken spar,
   And bound her to the mast.

"O father! I hear the church-bells ring,
   Oh say, what may it be?"
" 'Tis a fog-bell on a rock-bound coast!"—
   And he steered for the open sea.

"O father! I hear the sound of guns,
   Oh say, what may it be?"
"Some ship in distress, that cannot live
   In such an angry sea!"

"O father! I see a gleaming light,
   Oh say, what may it be?"
But the father answered never a word,
   A frozen corpse was he.

Lashed to the helm, all stiff and stark,
   With his face turned to the skies,
The lantern gleamed through the gleaming snow
   On his fixed and glassy eyes.

Then the maiden clasped her hands and prayed
   That savèd she might be;
And she thought of Christ, who stilled the wave,
   On the Lake of Galilee.

And fast through the midnight dark and drear,
   Through the whistling sleet and snow,
Like a sheeted ghost, the vessel swept
   Towards the reef of Norman's Woe.

And ever the fitful gusts between
   A sound came from the land;
It was the sound of the trampling surf,
   On the rocks and the hard sea-sand.

The breakers were right beneath her bows,
   She drifted a dreary wreck,
And a whooping billow swept the crew
   Like icicles from her deck.

She struck where the white and fleecy waves
   Looked soft as carded wool,
But the cruel rocks, they gored her side
   Like the horns of an angry bull.

Her rattling shrouds, all sheathed in ice,
   With the masts went by the board;
Like a vessel of glass, she stove and sank,
   Ho! ho! the breakers roared!

At daybreak, on the bleak sea-beach,
   A fisherman stood aghast,
To see the form of a maiden fair,
   Lashed close to a drifting mast.

The salt sea was frozen on her breast,
    The salt tears in her eyes;
And he saw her hair, like the brown sea-weed,
    On the billows fall and rise.

Such was the wreck of the Hesperus,
    In the midnight and the snow!
Christ save us all from a death like this
    On the reef of Norman's Woe!

This poem is based on a real occurrence. Longfellow read a newspaper account of a wreck on Norman's Reef off Gloucester. A body, lashed to a piece of wreckage, had been washed ashore along with the bodies of 20 other victims. The poet was deeply stirred, and his ballad conveys his feeling of compassion.

For seven stanzas Longfellow holds back the grim truth from the reader. When we realize that despite her innocence and trust, the little girl has not been saved, we woefully join in the prayer at the end of the story.

The simplicity of the recital has all the unremitting harshness of an angry sea. The short lines of this poem toll like a bell; inevitably there will come a message of doom.

ROSE HARTWICK THORPE (1850-1939)

This Indiana-born novelist specialized in sentimental tales. *Curfew*, written while Mrs. Thorpe was still in her teens, became an instantaneous success, and has been translated into many languages.

Curfew Must Not Ring Tonight

Slowly England's sun was setting o'er the hilltops
    far away,
Filling all the land with beauty at the close of
    one sad day;
And the last rays kissed the forehead of a man
    and maiden fair,
He with footsteps slow and weary, she with sunny
    floating hair;
He with bowed head, sad and thoughtful, she with
    lips all cold and white,
Struggling to keep back the murmur, "Curfew must
    not ring tonight!"

"Sexton," Bessie's white lips faltered, pointing to
    the prison old,
With its turrets tall and gloomy, with its walls,
    dark, damp and cold—

"I've a lover in the prison, doomed this very
          night to die
At the ringing of the curfew, and no earthly
          help is nigh.
Cromwell will not come till sunset"; and her
          face grew strangely white
As she breathed the husky whisper, "Curfew must
          not ring tonight!"

"Bessie," calmly spoke the sexton—and his accents
          pierced her heart
Like the piercing of an arrow, like a deadly
          poisoned dart—
"Long, long years I've rung the curfew from that
          gloomy, shadowed tower;
Every evening, just at sunset, it has told the
          twilight hour;
I have done my duty ever, tried to do it
          just and right—
Now I'm old I still must do it: Curfew, girl,
          must ring tonight!"

Wild her eyes and pale her features, stern and
          white her thoughtful brow,
And within her secret bosom Bessie made a
          solemn vow.
She had listened while the judges read, without a
          tear or sigh,

"At the ringing of the curfew, Basil Underwood
     must die."
And her breath came fast and faster, and her eyes
     grew large and bright,
As in undertone she murmured, "Curfew must
     not ring tonight!"

With quick step she bounded forward, sprang within
     the old church door,
Left the old man threading slowly paths he'd
     often trod before;
Not one moment paused the maiden, but with eye
     and cheek aglow
Mounted up the gloomy tower, where the bell
     swung to and fro
As she climbed the dusty ladder, on which fell no
     ray of light,
Up and up, her white lips saying, "Curfew shall
     not ring tonight!"

She has reached the topmost ladder, o'er her hangs
     the great dark bell:
Awful is the gloom beneath her like the pathway
     down to hell;
Lo, the ponderous tongue is swinging. 'Tis the
     hour of curfew now,
And the sight has chilled her bosom, stopped her
     breath and paled her brow;

Shall she let it ring? No, never! Flash her eyes
      with sudden light,
And she springs and grasps it firmly: "Curfew shall
      not ring tonight!"
Out she swung, far out; the city seemed a speck
      of light below;
She 'twixt heaven and earth suspended as the bell
      swung to and fro;
And the sexton at the bell rope, old and deaf,
      heard not the bell,
But he thought it still was ringing fair young
      Basil's funeral knell.

Still the maiden clung more firmly, and, with
trembling lips and white,
Said, to hush her heart's wild beating, "Curfew
shall not ring tonight!"

It was o'er; the bell ceased swaying, and the
    maiden stepped once more
Firmly on the dark old ladder, where for
    hundred years before
Human foot had not been planted; but the brave
    deed she had done
Should be told long ages after—often as the
    setting sun
Should illume the sky with beauty, aged sires,
    with heads of white,
Long should tell the little children, "Curfew did
    not ring that night."

O'er the distant hills came Cromwell; Bessie sees him,
    and her brow,
Full of hope and full of gladness, has no anxious
    traces now.

At his feet she tells her story, shows her hands all
      bruised and torn;
And her face so sweet and pleading, yet with
      sorrow pale and worn,
Touched his heart with sudden pity—lit his eye
      with misty light;
"Go, your lover lives!" said Cromwell; "Curfew
      shall not ring tonight!"

Bessie's lover is condemned for spying, and must die when the curfew bell tolls the hour of twilight. Only Cromwell, leader of the English Commonwealth, can save him. But Cromwell is not due to arrive in the town until sunset, AFTER *curfew.*

The aged sexton whose job it has been for many years to toll the bell cannot defer his duty—not even for the sake of the two young lovers. It is Bessie, then, who alone must save her sweetheart. Nor must she jeopardize the old man's position.

Follow Bessie as she climbs to the heights of the church tower, and climbs up into the belfry. Now as the sexton far below begins to pull on the bell-rope, Bessie grasps the clapper to muffle the iron ball with her body. Although the bell swings from side to side, it emits no sound.

And now she must hurry down to find Cromwell and plead for the life of her young man. Only when the stern, old Puritan himself takes up the refrain "CURFEW SHALL NOT RING TONIGHT" *is the rescue of Basil Underwood confirmed.*

Born in England, Morris, when a boy, loved the stories about the Middle Ages.

As an architect, he sought to bring back to England the medieval style. As a writer, he attempted to develop interest in pre-Renaissance art. Interested, too, in medieval epic poetry, he translated such poems as the "Fall of the Nieblungs," using such poems as models for his own compositions.

Shameful Death

There were four of us about that bed;
  The mass-priest knelt at the side,
I and his mother stood at the head,
  Over his feet lay the bride;
We were quite sure that he was dead,
  Though his eyes were open wide.

He did not die in the night,
  He did not die in the day,
But in the morning twilight
  His spirit pass'd away,
When neither sun nor moon was bright,
  And the trees were merely grey.

He was not slain with the sword,
  Knight's axe, or the knightly spear,
Yet spoke he never a word
  After he came in here;
I cut away the cord
  From the neck of my brother dear.

He did not strike one blow,
  For the recreants came behind,
In a place where the hornbeams grow,
  A path right hard to find,
For the hornbeam boughs swing so,
  That the twilight makes it blind.

They lighted a great torch then,
  When his arms were pinion'd fast,
Sir John the knight of the Fen,
  Sir Guy of the Dolorous Blast,
With knights threescore and ten,
  Hung brave Lord Hugh at last.

I am threescore and ten,
  And my hair is all turn'd grey,
But I met Sir John of the Fen
  Long ago on a summer day,
And am glad to think of the moment when
  I took his life away.

I am threescore and ten,
   And my strength is mostly pass'd,
But long ago I and my men,
   When the sky was overcast,
And the smoke roll'd over the reeds of the fen,
   Slew Guy of the Dolorous Blast.

And now, knights all of you,
   I pray you pray for Sir Hugh,
A good knight and a true,
   And for Alice, his wife, pray too.

Young Lord Hugh was a victim of clan rivalry. He has met a shameful death. To die bravely in battle is sad—yes—but honorable; but to be hoisted up on a tree like a criminal is ignominious.

The narrator boasts that he did not let the foul deed go unpunished. Even though he is seventy, he is proud of his precious memory. Revenge is part of the folk ethic of his day.

The older brother relates how he met Sir John and Sir Guy, leaders of the opposing clan, and how he struck them both down—for the sake of Sir Hugh; the one to avenge his young brother's death; the other, to avenge the shameful manner of his dying.

With no interest in schooling until he heard verses from the Scottish poet Burns read aloud, Whittier thereafter became self-educated.

Eventually, he rose to great prominence as the poet of the Abolitionist movement, serving as secretary of the American Anti-slavery Society, and writing a poem a week on freedom.

Whittier was born in Massachusetts. He never married. He lived simply, worked steadily, and gave all the money he earned to charity.

Barbara Frietchie

Up from the meadows rich with corn,
Clear in the cool September morn,

The clustered spires of Frederick stand
Green-walled by the hills of Maryland.

Round about them orchards sweep,
Apple and peach tree fruited deep,

Fair as the garden of the Lord
To the eyes of the famished rebel horde,

On that pleasant morn of the early fall
When Lee marched over the mountain wall;

Over the mountains winding down,
Horse and foot, into Frederick town.

Forty flags with their silver stars,
Forty flags with their crimson bars,

Flapped in the morning wind: the sun
Of noon looked down, and saw not one.

Up rose old Barbara Frietchie then,
Bowed with her fourscore years and ten;

Bravest of all in Frederick town,
She took up the flag the men hauled down;

In her attic window the staff she set,
To show that one heart was loyal yet.

Up the street came the rebel tread.
Stonewall Jackson riding ahead.

Under his slouched hat left and right
He glanced; the old flag met his sight.

"Halt!"—the dust-brown ranks stood fast,
"Fire"—out blazed the rifle-blast.

It shivered the window, pane and sash;
It rent the banner with seam and gash.

She leaned far out on the window-sill,
And shook it forth with a royal will.

"Shoot, if you must, this old gray head,
But spare your country's flag," she said.

A shade of sadness, a blush of shame,
Over the face of the leader came;

The nobler nature within him stirred
To life at that woman's deed and word;

"Who touches a hair of yon gray head
Dies like a dog! March on!" he said.

Quick as it fell, from the broken staff
Dame Barbara snatched the silken scarf.

All day long through Frederick street
Sounded the tread of marching feet:

All day long that free flag tossed
Over the heads of the rebel host.

Ever its torn folds rose and fell
On the loyal winds that loved it well;

And through the hill-gaps sunset light
Shone over it with a warm good-night.

Barbara Frietchie's work is o'er,
And the Rebel rides on his raids no more.

Honor to her! and let a tear
Fall, for her sake, on Stonewall's bier.

Over Barbara Frietchie's grave,
Flag of Freedom and Union, wave!

Peace and order and beauty draw
Round thy symbol of light and law;

And ever the stars above look down
On thy stars below in Frederick town!

Whittier's BARBARA FRIETCHIE *has become standard reading in almost every schoolroom throughout the land. There is something universally appealing in the heroine's act of defiance which drew cheers even from the man she had affronted.*

Note how the couplets lend a marching rhythm, best illustrated in the two lines:

> *All day long through Frederick street*
> *Sounded the tread of marching feet:*

There is undoubtedly more fiction than fact in this stirring poem. We may find it hard to believe that Dame Barbara was such a marvelous catcher that she was able to snatch the flag in the very instant that it fell from the flagpole, in the face of the fact that the soldiers' bullets broke the window and the flagpole, and of course, would have hit her, too, if she were at the scene. Nevertheless, we can still applaud her aplomb. If the poet's facts are inaccurate, the patriotic message is nevertheless quite clear.

JOHN GODFREY SAXE (1816-1887)

Born in Vermont, the son of a mill-owner, Saxe was educated for the law. He served the public as a Superintendent
of Schools, as a State's Attorney, and as a United States
Collector of Customs.

   After his humorous verses began to frequently
appear in magazines, he moved to New York where he
was in constant demand as a genial after-dinner speaker.
His wit and good humor made him a popular figure in his
day.

The Blind Men and the Elephant

A HINDOO FABLE

It was six men of Indostan
   To learning much inclined,
Who went to see the Elephant
   (Though all of them were blind),
That each by observation
   Might satisfy his mind.

The *First* approached the Elephant,
   And happening to fall
Against his broad and sturdy side,
   At once began to bawl:
"God bless me! but the Elephant
   Is very like a wall!"

The *Second*, feeling of the tusk,
  Cried, "Ho! what have we here
So very round and smooth and sharp?
  To me 'tis mighty clear
This wonder of an Elephant
  Is very like a spear!"

The *Third* approached the animal,
  And happening to take
The squirming trunk within his hands,
  Thus boldly up and spake:
"I see," quoth he, "the Elephant
  Is very like a snake!"

The *Fourth* reached out an eager hand,
  And felt about the knee.
"What most this wondrous beast is like
  Is mighty plain," quoth he;
" 'Tis clear enough the Elephant
  Is very like a tree!"

The *Fifth* who chanced to touch the ear,
  Said: "E'en the blindest man
Can tell what this resembles most;
  Deny the fact who can,
This marvel of an Elephant
  Is very like a fan!"

The *Sixth* no sooner had begun
  About the beast to grope,

Than, seizing on the swinging tail
  That fell within his scope,
"I see," quoth he, "the Elephant
  Is very like a rope!"
And so these men of Indostan
  Disputed loud and long,
Each in his own opinion
  Exceeding stiff and strong,
Though each was partly in the right,
  And all were in the wrong!

THE MORAL:

So oft in theologic wars,
  The disputants, I ween,
Rail on in utter ignorance
  Of what each other mean,
And prate about an Elephant
  Not one of them has seen!

*Here is excellent ironic comment on how people are wont
to defend an opinion based on partial—and therefore in-
sufficient—evidence.*

He was born in England, the youngest child of twelve, and became an artist. At first, he earned his living as a draughts-man for the Zoological Society of London.

The Earl of Derby saw Lear drawing, and asked him to come to his country estate to sketch the birds there. It turned out that Lear made his home with the Earl for many years. To amuse the children of his patron, he wrote nonsense verses. His limericks are famous.

The Owl and the Pussycat

The Owl and the Pussy-Cat went to sea
  In a beautiful pea-green boat,
They took some honey, and plenty of money,
  Wrapped up in a five-pound note.
The Owl looked up to the stars above,
  And sang to a small guitar,
"O lovely Pussy! O Pussy, my love,
  What a beautiful Pussy you are,
      You are,
      You are!
What a beautiful Pussy you are!"

Pussy said to the Owl, "You elegant fowl!
   How charmingly sweet you sing!
O let us be married! too long we have tarried:
   But what shall we do for a ring?"
They sailed away for a year and a day,
   To the land where the Bong-tree grows,
And there in a wood a Piggy-wig stood,
   With a ring at the end of his nose,
      His nose,
      His nose,
With a ring at the end of his nose.

"Dear Pig, are you willing to sell for one shilling
   Your ring?" Said the Piggy, "I will."
So they took it away, and were married next day
   By the Turkey who lives on the hill.
They dinèd on mince, and slices of quince,
   Which they ate with a runcible spoon;
And hand in hand, on the edge of the sand,
   They danced by the light of the moon,
         The moon,
         The moon,
They danced by the light of the moon.

*Much of this poem's effect comes from sprightly rhythm;
"The Owl and the Pussycat" is written in dance time, in
imitation of a quick jig.*

   *P.S. A runcible spoon is a kind of fork having three
broad tines.*

ROBERT BROWNING (1812-1889)

While still a child, Browning began to write little poems and plays, reading steadily from his father's well-stocked library. Taught at home by a tutor, his studies included music, singing, dancing, riding, boxing, and fencing.

In 1846, he eloped with Elizabeth Barret, whose reputation as a poet far exceeded his. They lived for 16 years in Italy. After her death, Browning returned to England to win fame and fortune in his own right.

The Pied Piper of Hamelin

Hamelin Town's in Brunswick,
By famous Hanover city;
    The river Weser, deep and wide,
    Washes its wall on the southern side;
    A pleasanter spot you never spied;
But, when begins my ditty,
    Almost five hundred years ago,
    To see the townsfolk suffer so
From vermin was a pity.

    Rats!
They fought the dogs, and kill'd the cats,
    And bit the babies in the cradles,
And ate the cheeses out of the vats,
And lick'd the soup from the cook's own ladles,

Split open the kegs of salted sprats,
Made nests inside men's Sunday hats,
And even spoil'd the women's chats,
    By drowning their speaking
    With shrieking and squeaking
In fifty different sharps and flats.

At last the people in a body
    To the Town Hall came flocking:
" 'Tis clear," cried they, "our Mayor's a noddy;
    And as for our Corporation—shocking
To think we buy gowns lined with ermine
For dolts that can't or won't determine
What's best to rid us of our vermin!
You hope, because you're old and obese,
To find in the furry civic robe ease?
Rouse up, sirs! Give your brains a racking
To find the remedy we're lacking,
Or, sure as fate, we'll send you packing!"
At this the Mayor and Corporation
Quaked with a mighty consternation.
An hour they sate in counsel,
    At length the Mayor broke silence:
"For a guilder I'd my ermine gown sell;
    I wish I were a mile hence!
It's easy to bid one rack one's brain—
I'm sure my poor head aches again,
I've scratch'd it so, and all in vain.

Oh for a trap, a trap, a trap!"
Just as he said this, what should hap
At the chamber-door but a gentle tap?
"Bless us!" cried the Mayor, "What's that?"
(With the Corporation as he sat,
Looking little though wondrous fat;
Nor brighter was his eye, nor moister
Than a too long-open'd oyster,
Save when at noon his paunch grew mutinous
For a plate of turtle, green and glutinous)
"Only a scraping of shoes on the mat?
Anything like the sound of a rat
Makes my heart go pit-a-pat!"

"Come in!"—the Mayor cried, looking bigger:
And in did come the strangest figure!
His queer long coat from heel to head
Was half of yellow and half of red;
And he himself was tall and thin,
With sharp blue eyes, each like a pin,
And light loose hair, yet swarthy skin,
No tuft on cheek nor beard on chin,
But lips where smiles went out and in—
There was no guessing his kith and kin!

And nobody could enough admire
The tall man and his quaint attire:
Quoth one: "It's as if my great-grandsire,
Starting up at the Trump of Doom's tone,
Had walk'd this way from his painted tombstone!"

He advanced to the council-table:
And, "Please your honors," said he, "I'm able,
By means of a secret charm, to draw
All creatures living beneath the sun,
That creep, or swim, or fly, or run,
After me so as you never saw!
And I chiefly use my charm
On creatures that do people harm,
The mole, and toad, and newt, and viper;
And people call me the Pied Piper."
(And here they noticed round his neck
A scarf of red and yellow stripe,
To match with his coat of the selfsame check;
And at the scarf's end hung a pipe;
And his fingers, they noticed, were ever straying
As if impatient to be playing
Upon this pipe, as low it dangled
Over his vesture so old-fangled.)
"Yet," said he, "poor piper as I am,
In Tartary I freed the Cham,
Last June, from his huge swarm of gnats;
I eased in Asia the Nizam

Of a monstrous brood of vampyre bats;
And, as for what your brain bewilders—
If I can rid your town of rats,
Will you give me a thousand guilders?"
"One? fifty thousand!" was the exclamation
Of the astonished Mayor and Corporation.

Into the street the Piper stept,
    Smiling first a little smile,
As if he knew what magic slept
    In his quiet pipe the while;
Then, like a musical adept,
To blow the pipe his lips he wrinkled,
And green and blue his sharp eyes twinkled,
Like a candle-flame where salt is sprinkled;
And ere three shrill notes the pipe had utter'd,
You heard as if an army mutter'd;
And the muttering grew to a grumbling;
And the grumbling grew to a mighty rumbling;
And out of the houses the rats came tumbling.
Great rats, small rats, lean rats, brawny rats,
Brown rats, black rats, gray rats, tawny rats,
Grave old plodders, gay young friskers,
    Fathers, mothers, uncles, cousins,
Cocking tails and prickling whiskers,
    Families by tens and dozens,
Brothers, sisters, husbands, wives—
Follow'd the Piper for their lives.

From street to street he piped advancing,
And step for step they follow'd dancing,
Until they came to the river Weser,
Wherein all plunged and perish'd,
Save one who, stout as Julius Caesar,
Swam across and lived to carry
(As the manuscript he cherish'd)

To Rat-land home his commentary,
Which was, "At the first shrill notes of the pipe,
I heard a sound as of scraping tripe,
And putting apples, wondrous ripe,
Into a cider press's gripe:
And a moving away of pickle-tub boards,
And a leaving ajar of conserve-cupboards,

And a drawing the corks of train-oil flasks,
And a breaking the hoops of butter-casks;
And it seemed as if a voice
(Sweeter far than by harp or by psaltery
Is breathed) call'd out, O rats, rejoice!
The world is grown to one vast dry-saltery!
So munch on, crunch on, take your nuncheon,
Breakfast, supper, dinner, luncheon!
And just as a bulky sugar-puncheon,
All ready staved, like a great sun shone
Glorious scarce an inch before me,
Just as methought it said, Come, bore me!
I found the Weser rolling o'er me."

You should have heard the Hamelin people
Ringing the bells till they rock'd the steeple;
"Go," cried the Mayor, "and get long poles!
Consult with carpenters and builders,
And leave in our town not even a trace
Of the rats!"—when suddenly up the face
Of the Piper perk'd in the market-place,
With a, "First, if you please, my thousand guilders!"

A thousand guilders! The Mayor look'd blue;
So did the Corporation too.
For council dinners made rare havoc
With Claret, Moselle, Vin-de-Grave, Hock;
And half the money would replenish

Their cellar's biggest butt with Rhenish.
To pay this sum to a wandering fellow
With a gypsy coat of red and yellow!
"Beside," quoth the Mayor, with a knowing wink,
"Our business was done at the river's brink;
We saw with our eyes the vermin sink,
And what's dead can't come to life, I think.
So, friend, we're not the folks to shrink
From the duty of giving you something for drink,
And a matter of money to put in your poke;
But, as for the guilders, what we spoke
Of them, as you very well know, was in joke.
Beside, our losses have made us thrifty;
A thousand guilders! Come, take fifty!"

The Piper's face fell and he cried,
"No trifling! I can't wait! beside,
I've promised to visit by dinner-time
Bagdad, and accept the prime
Of the Head Cook's pottage, all he's rich in,
For having left, in the Caliph's kitchen,
Of a nest of scorpions no survivor—
With him I proved no bargain-driver.
With you, don't think I'll bate a stiver!
And folks who put me in a passion
May find me pipe to another fashion."

"How?" cried the Mayor, "d'ye think I'll brook
Being worse treated than a Cook?

Insulted by a lazy ribald
With idle pipe and vesture piebald?
You threaten us, fellow? Do your worst,
Blow your pipe there till you burst!"

Once more he stept into the street;
    And to his lips again
    Laid his long pipe of smooth straight cane;

And ere he blew three notes (such sweet
Soft notes as yet musician's cunning
   Never gave the enraptured air)

There was a rustling, that seem'd like a bustling
Of merry crowds justling at pitching and hustling,
Small feet were pattering, wooden shoes clattering,
Little hands clapping, and little tongues chattering,
And, like fowls in a farm-yard when barley
      is scattering,
Out came the children running.
All the little boys and girls,
With rosy cheeks and flaxen curls,
And sparkling eyes and teeth like pearls,

Tripping and skipping, ran merrily after
The wonderful music with shouting and laughter.

The Mayor was dumb, and the Council stood
As if they were changed into blocks of wood,
Unable to move a step, or cry
To the children merrily skipping by—
And could only follow with the eye
That joyous crowd at the Piper's back.
But how the Mayor was on the rack,
And the wretched Council's bosoms beat,
As the Piper turn'd from the High Street
To where the Weser roll'd its waters
Right in the way of their sons and daughters!
However, he turned from south to west,
And to Koppelberg Hill his steps address'd,
And after him the children press'd;
Great was the joy in every breast.
"He never can cross that mighty top!
He's forced to let the piping drop,
And we shall see our children stop!"
When, lo, as they reach'd the mountain side,
A wondrous portal open'd wide,
As if a cavern was suddenly hollow'd;
And the Piper advanced and the children follow'd,
And when all were in to the very last,
The door in the mountain-side shut fast.
Did I say all? No! one was lame,

And could not dance the whole of the way,
And in after years, if you would blame
His sadness, he was used to say,
"It's dull in our town since my playmates left!
I can't forget that I'm bereft
Of all the pleasant sights they see,
Which the Piper also promised me,
For he led us, he said, to a joyous land,
Joining the town and just at hand,
Where waters gush'd and fruit trees grew,
And flowers put forth a fairer hue,
And everything was strange and new;
The sparrows were brighter than peacocks here,
And the dogs outran our fallow deer,
And honey-bees had lost their stings,
And horses were born with eagles' wings;
And just as I became assured
My lame foot would be speedily cured,
The music stopp'd, and I stood still,
And found myself outside the Hill,
Left alone against my will,
To go now limping as before,
And never hear of that country more!"

Alas, alas for Hamelin!
    There came into many a burgher's pate
    A text which says that Heaven's Gate
    Opes to the rich at as easy rate

As the needle's eye takes a camel in!
The Mayor sent east, west, north, and south
To offer the Piper by word of mouth,
   Wherever it was men's lot to find him,
Silver and gold to his heart's content,
If he'd only return the way he went,
   And bring the children behind him.
But when they saw 'twas a lost endeavor,
And Piper and dancers were gone forever,
They made a decree that lawyers never
   Should think their records dated duly
If, after the day of the month and year,
These words did not as well appear:
"And so long after what happen'd here
   On the twenty-second of July,
Thirteen hundred and Seventy-six;"
And the better in memory to fix
The place of the children's last retreat,
They call'd it the Pied Piper's Street,
Where any one playing on pipe or tabor
Was sure for the future to lose his labor.
Nor suffer'd they hostelry or tavern
   To shock with mirth a street so solemn,
But opposite the place of the cavern
   They wrote the story on a column,
And on the great church-window painted
The same, to make the world acquainted
How their children were stolen away,

And there it stands to this very day.
And I must not omit to say
That in Transylvania there's a tribe
Of alien people that ascribe
The outlandish ways and dress
On which their neighbors lay such stress,
To their fathers and mothers having risen
Out of some subterranean prison,
Into which they were trepann'd
Long time ago in a mighty band
Out of Hamelin town in Brunswick land,
But how or why, they don't understand.

So, Willy, let you and me be wipers
Of scores out with all men—especially pipers;
And, whether they pipe us free, from rats
    or from mice,
If we've promised them aught, let us keep
    our promise.

How skillfully the poet changes his rhythms from line to line. Nor does Browning constrict himself by the limitations of a stanza form: he lengthens or shortens his stanza according to the action and the needs of the story. The result of this poetical free wheeling is that the story comes alive and flows on quite naturally to its climax. In a long poem like this, a constant rhythm might prove boring. Browning sidesteps this pitfall in a masterful manner.

JONATHAN SWIFT (1667-1745)

Swift grew up in Ireland. He followed the profession of a clergyman.

Well known for his satirical writings, his most famous work is *Gulliver's Travels* in which he made fun of the foibles and corruption of his day.

Baucis and Philemon

In ancient times, as story tells,
The saints would often leave their cells,
And stroll about, but hid their quality,
To try good people's hospitality.
It happened on a winter night,
As authors of the legend write,
Two brother hermits, saints by trade,
Taking their tour in masquerade,
Disguised in tattered garments went
To a small village down in Kent;
Where in the stroller's canting strain,
They begged from door to door in vain;
Tried every tone might pity win,
But not a soul would take them in.

Our wandering saints, in woeful state,
Treated at this ungodly rate,

Having through all the village passed,
To a small cottage came at last.
Where dwelt a good old honest yeoman,
Call'd in the neighborhood Philemon;
Who kindly did these saints invite
In his poor hut to pass the night;
And then the hospitable sire
Bid goodly Baucis mend the fire;
While he from out the chimney took
A flitch of bacon off the hook,
And freely from the fattest side
Cut out large slices to be fried;
Then stepped aside to fetch them drink,
Filled a large jug up to the brink,
And saw it fairly twice go round;
Yet (what is wonderful) they found
'Twas still replenished to the top,
As if they ne'er had touched a drop.
The good old couple were amazed,
And often on each other gazed;
For both were frightened to the heart,
And just began to cry, "What art!"
Then softly turned aside to view
Whether the lights were burning blue.

"Good folks, ye need not be afraid;
We are but saints," the hermits said;

"No hurt shall come to you or yours;
But for that pack of churlish boors,
Not fit to live on Christian ground,
They and their houses shall be drowned;
Whilst you shall see your cottage rise,
And grow a church before your eyes."

They scarce had spoke, when fair and soft,
The roof began to mount aloft,
Aloft rose every beam and rafter,
The heavy wall climbed slowly after;
The chimney widened and grew higher,
Became a steeple with a spire.
The kettle to the top was hoist,
And there stood fastened to a joist;
Doomed ever in suspense to dwell,
'Tis now no kettle, but a bell.

A woden jack which had almost
Lost by disuse the art to roast,

A sudden alteration feels,
Increased by new intestine wheels;
The jack and chimney, near allied,
Had never left each other's side:
The chimney to a steeple grown,
The jack would not be left alone;
But up against the steeple reared,
Became a clock, and still adhered.
The groaning chair began to crawl,
Like a huge snail, along the wall;
There stuck aloft in public view,
And with small change a pulpit grew.
The cottage, by such feats as these,
Grown to a church by just degrees,
The hermits then desired the host
To ask for what he fancied most.
Philemon, having paused a while,
Returned them thanks in homely style:
"I'm old, and fain would live at ease;
Make me the parson, if you please."

The poem BAUCIS AND PHILEMON *is based on an old Greek legend. Jonathan Swift slyly changes the locale from ancient Hellas to "a small village down in Kent."*

This whimsical attitude runs throughout the poem. We are quite delighted—but not surprised—when Philemon, asked to name his heart's desire, makes it clear that the unharried life of a parson seems to him to be the height of bliss.

W. S. GILBERT (1836-1911)

He was born in London as the son of a retired naval surgeon. He worked first as a government clerk and then as a lawyer; but after a while, he abandoned law for literature.

By 1877, he had written over 20 plays. He joined forces with the well-known composer, Arthur Sullivan; and today, the operettas of the famous "Gilbert and Sullivan" team are sung in every corner of the world.

The Yarn of the Nancy Bell

'Twas on the shores that round our coast
    From Deal to Ramsgate span,
That I found alone, on a piece of stone,
    An elderly naval man.

His hair was weedy, his beard was long,
    And weedy and long was he;
And I heard this wight on the shore recite
    In a singular minor key:

"Oh, I am a cook and a captain bold,
    And the mate of the Nancy brig,
And a bo'sun tight, and a midshipmite,
    And the crew of the captain's gig."

And he shook his fists and he tore his hair,
   Till I really felt afraid,
For I couldn't help thinking the man
     had been drinking,
   And so I simply said:

"O elderly man, it's little I know
   Of the duties of men of the sea,
And I'll eat my hand if I understand
   How ever you can be

"At once a cook and a captain bold,
   And the mate of the Nancy brig,
And a bo'sun tight, and a midshipmite,
   And the crew of the captain's gig!"

Then he gave a hitch to his trowsers, which
    Is a trick all seamen larn,
And having got rid of a thumping quid,
    He spun this painful yarn:

" 'Twas in the good ship Nancy Bell
    That we sail'd to the Indian sea,
And there on a reef we come to grief,
    Which has often occurr'd to me.

"And pretty nigh all o' the crew was drown'd
    (There was seventy-seven o' soul);
And only ten of the Nancy's men
    Said 'Here!' to the muster-roll.

"There was me, and the cook, and the captain bold,
    And the mate of the Nancy brig,
And the bo'sun tight and a midshipmite,
    And the crew of the captain's gig.

"For a month we'd neither vittles nor drink,
　　Till a-hungry we did feel,
So we draw'd a lot, and, accordin', shot
　　The captain for our meal.

"The next lot fell to the Nancy's mate,
　　And a delicate dish he made;
Then our appetite with the midshipmite
　　We seven survivors stay'd.

"And then we murder'd the bo'sun tight,
　　And he much resembled pig;
Then we vittled free, did the cook and me,
　　On the crew of the captain's gig.

"Then only the cook and me was left,
　　And the delicate question, 'Which
Of us two goes to the kettle?' arose,
　　And we argued it out as sich.

"For I loved that cook as a brother, I did,
　　And the cook he worshipp'd me;
But we'd both be blow'd if we'd either be stow'd
　　In the other chap's hold, you see.

" 'I'll be eat if you dines off me,' says Tom.
　　'Yes, that,' says I, 'you'll be.
I'm boil'd if I die, my friend,' quoth I;
　　And 'Exactly so,' quoth he.

"Says he: 'Dear James, to murder me
    Were a foolish thing to do,
For don't you see that you can't cook *me*,
    While I can—and will—cook *you?*'

"So he boils the water, and takes the salt
    And the pepper in portions true
(Which he never forgot), and some chopp'd shallot,
    And some sage and parsley too.

"'Come here,' says he, with a proper pride,
    Which his smiling features tell;
''Twill soothing be if I let you see
    How extremely nice you'll smell.'

"And he stirr'd it round and round and round,
    And he sniff'ed at the foaming froth;
When I ups with his heels, and smothers
       his squeals
    In the scum of the boiling broth.

"And I eat that cook in a week or less,
    And as I eating be
The last of his chops, why I almost drops,
    For a vessel in sight I see.

"And I never larf, and I never smile,
    And I never lark nor play;

But I sit and croak, and a single joke
  I have—which is to say:

"Oh, I am a cook and a captain bold,
  And the mate of the Nancy brig,
And a bo'sun tight, and a midshipmite,
  And the crew of the captain's gig!"

The poet uses the middle rhyme in the third sentence of each quatrain to lend an extra fillip to the rhythm. Ordinarily, the story of a man being scalded alive would excite horror, but the poet is so whimsical and deft that a spirit of fun is immediately created, and you know that it's all a great big joke.

LULU E. THOMPSON (1839-1916)

In Hardin County

With flintlocked guns and polished stocks,
Knee breeches and long homespun socks,
On morning of St. Valentine
Two hunters met in 1809.
Across the line from Illinois;
They stopped their mules and voiced their joy.

"Why, Ben, it's been a quite a spell
Since I've seen you. The folks all well?
Bring any news from up near town?"
"Why, yes. D'you know John Ezry Brown?
They say that he's a-goin' down
To Washington in all the din
To see Jim Madison sworn in.

"And this young feller Bonaparte
That's fightin' cross the sea,
Is slicin' Europe all to bits.
Least that's what they're a-tellin' me."
"Wal, wal, nice day, kinda breezy
This mule's gettin' quite uneasy.

"Now come and see us some time, do,
And bring the gals and Hepsy, too."
"Yes, some fine day we'll be along,
Got any news to send along?"
"No, nothin' worth a tinker's song.
There's nothin' happens here near me,
Doggondest place you ever see.

"Tom Lincoln lives right over there,
In that log cabin, bleak and bare,
They say they have a little babe,
I understand they've named him 'Abe.'
Yes, Sally said just 'tother day,
That nothin' happens down this way."

This poem is organized around the idea of contrast. The two Hardin County hunters pair off names like Bonaparte and Hepsy; they couple remarks like "slicin' Europe all to bits" and "nice day, kinda breezy;" they intermingle private affairs and public affairs, the health of their folks with the presidential inauguration.

One event that is just a small piece of local news is destined to become significant in American history. By the time Napoleon is dead and gone, Abe Lincoln will be sworn in as President of the United States. The present becomes contrasted with the future.

Charles Lutwidge Dodgson was a child prodigy, interested in mathematics and in literature. Before he was twelve, he wrote plays for marionettes. For most of his life, he taught math at Oxford.

In 1865, Dodgson wrote *Alice in Wonderland* to amuse a young girl he had befriended. This book was published under the pen name of Lewis Carroll. Originally, it was regarded as a child's story, but was later recognized as a masterpiece of satire. *The Walrus and the Carpenter* appears in that book as one of its many ironic and seemingly nonsensical episodes.

The Walrus and the Carpenter

The sun was shining on the sea,
  Shining with all his might:
He did his very best to make
  The billows smooth and bright—
And this was odd, because it was
  The midle of the night.

The moon was shining sulkily,
  Because she thought the sun
Had got no business to be there
  After the day was done—
"It's very rude of him," she said,
  "To come and spoil the fun!"

138

The sea was wet as wet could be,
  The sands were dry as dry.
You could not see a cloud, because
  No cloud was in the sky:
No birds were flying overhead—
  There were no birds to fly.

The Walrus and the Carpenter
  Were walking close at hand:
They wept like anything to see
  Such quantities of sand.
"If this were only cleared away,"
  They said, "it *would* be grand!"

"If seven maids with seven mops
   Swept it for half a year,
Do you suppose," the Walrus said,
   "That they could get it clear?"
"I doubt it," said the Carpenter,
   And shed a bitter tear.

"O Oysters, come and walk with us!"
   The Walrus did beseech.
"A pleasant talk, a pleasant walk,
   Along the briny beach:
We cannot do with more than four,
   To give a hand to each."

The eldest Oyster looked at him,
   But never a word he said:
The eldest Oyster winked his eye,
   And shook his heavy head—
Meaning to say he did not choose
   To leave the oyster-bed.

But four young Oysters hurried up,
   All eager for the treat:
Their coats were brushed, their faces washed,
   Their shoes were clean and neat—
And this was odd, because, you know,
   They hadn't any feet.

Four other Oysters followed them,
    And yet another four;
And thick and fast they came at last,
    And more, and more, and more—
All hopping through the frothy waves,
    And scrambling to the shore.

The Walrus and the Carpenter
    Walked on a mile or so,
And then they rested on a rock
    Conveniently low:
And all the little Oysters stood
    And waited in a row.

"The time has come," the Walrus said,
   "To talk of many things:
Of shoes and ships and sealing-wax,
   Of cabbages and kings;
And why the sea is boiling hot—
   And whether pigs have wings."

"But wait a bit," the Oysters cried,
   "Before we have our chat;
For some of us are out of breath,
   And all of us are fat!"
"No hurry!" said the Carpenter.
   They thanked him much for that.

"A loaf of bread," the Walrus said,
  "Is what we chiefly need:
Pepper and vinegar besides
  Are very good indeed—
Now, if you're ready, Oysters dear,
  We can begin to feed."

"But not on us!" the Oysters cried,
  Turning a little blue.
"After such kindness, that would be
  A dismal thing to do!"
"The night is fine," the Walrus said.
  "Do you admire the view?

"It was so kind of you to come!
  And you are very nice!"
The Carpenter said nothng but
  "Cut us another slice.
I wish you were not quite so deaf—
  I've had to ask you twice!"

"It seems a shame," the Walrus said,
  "To play them such a trick,
After we've brought them out so far,
  And made them trot so quick!"
The Carpenter said nothing but
  "The butter's spread too thick!"

"I weep for you," the Walrus said:
   "I deeply sympathize."
With sobs and tears he sorted out
   Those of the largest size,
Holding his pocket-handkerchief
   Before his streaming eyes.

"O Oysters," said the Carpenter,
"You've had a pleasant run!
Shall we be trotting home again?"
   But answer came there none—
And this was scarcely odd, because
   They'd eaten every one.

The very title of this poem presents us with the strangest combination; and within the poem, statements too ridiculous to be believed and truths too obvious to be mentioned are presented with equal seriousness. Is there any sense or order in these lines?

The poet has presented a humorous charade in which he burlesques the human scene. The walrus and the carpenter behave as most people act and behave. They shed tears over the fact that things are not as they should be. But they nevertheless lure their own subsistence through trickery and guile.

And sure enough, there are any number of foolish oysters ready to come along and be tricked. To the very end, the walrus bewails injustice, but the carpenter wastes precious little time with his companion's talk and tears. When it comes down to it, they both eat their fill.

Lewis Carroll has made us laugh at every man, at the actions that hypocritically pass for justice, and at the specious ideas that pass for reason.

THOMAS BABINGTON MACAULAY (1800-1859)

Known as a historian, statesman, orator, and essayist, Macaulay won new popularity as a poet when he published his series of long narrative poems, *Lays of Ancient Rome,* in 1842. *Horatius* is probably the best-known of the four poems in the series, all of which follow the style of ancient Roman ballads.

Macaulay was born in Leicestershire, England, and was educated at Cambridge. At the age of 30, he was elected to Parliament. He remained a forceful leader of the Whig party throughout his life. In 1857, two years before his death, Queen Victoria named him Baron Macaulay of Rothley.

Horatius

LARS PORSENA of Clusium
    By the Nine Gods he swore
That the great house of Tarquin
    Should suffer wrong no more.
By the Nine Gods he swore it,
    And named a trysting day,
And bade his messengers ride forth,
East and west and south and north,
    To summon his array.

East and west and south and north
    The messengers ride fast,

146

And tower and town and cottage
  Have heard the trumpet's blast.
Shame on the false Etruscan
  Who lingers in his home
When Porsena of Clusium
  Is on the march for Rome.

The horsemen and the footmen
  Are pouring in amain,
From many a stately market-place;
  From many a fruitful plain;
From many a lonely hamlet,
  Which, hid by beech and pine,
Like an eagle's nest, hangs on the crest
  Of purple Apennine.

And now hath every city
  Sent up her tale of men;
The foot are fourscore thousand,
  The horse are thousands ten.
Before the gates of Sutrium
  Is met the great array.
A proud man was Lars Porsena
  Upon the trysting day.

For all the Etruscan armies
  Were ranged beneath his eye,
And many a banished Roman,

And many a stout ally;
And with a mighty following
　　To join the muster came
The Tusculan Mamilius,
　　Prince of the Latian name.

But by the yellow Tiber
　　Was tumult and affright:
From all the spacious champaign
　　To Rome men took their flight.
A mile around the city,
　　The throng stopped up the ways;
A fearful sight it was to see
　　Through two long nights and days.

For aged folk on crutches,
　　And women great with child,
And mothers sobbing over babes
　　That clung to them and smiled,
And sick men borne in litters
　　High on the necks of slaves,
And troops of sun-burned husbandmen
　　With reaping-hooks and staves.

And droves of mules and asses
　　Laden with skins of wine,
And endless flocks of goats and sheep,
　　And endless herds of kine,

And endless trains of wagons
   That creaked beneath the weight
Of corn-sacks and of household goods,
   Choked every roaring gate.

Now from the rock Tarpeian,
   Could the wan burghers spy
The line of blazing villages
   Red in the midnight sky.
The Fathers of the City,
   They sat all night and day,
For every hour some horseman came
   With tidings of dismay.

To eastward and to westward
   Have spread the Tuscan bands;
Nor house, nor fence, nor dovecote
   In Crustumerium stands.
Verbenna down to Ostia
   Hath wasted all the plain;
Astur hath stormed Janiculum,
   And the stout guards are slain.

I wis, in all the Senate,
   There was no heart so bold,
But sore it ached, and fast it beat,
   When that ill news was told.
Forthwith up rose the Consul,

Up rose the Fathers all;
In haste they girded up their gowns,
    And hied them to the wall.

They held a council standing
    Before the River-gate;
Short time was there, ye well may guess,
    For musing or debate.
Out spake the Consul roundly:
    "The bridge must straight go down;
For, since Janiculum is lost,
    Naught else can save the town."

Just then a scout came flying,
　　All wild with haste and fear:
"To arms! to arms! Sir Consul;
　　Lars Porsena is here."
On the low hills to westward
　　The Consul fixed his eye,
And saw the swarthy storm of dust
　　Rise fast along the sky.

And nearer fast and nearer
　　Doth the red whirlwind come;
And louder still, and still more loud
From underneath that rolling cloud,
Is heard the trumpet's war-note proud,

The trampling, and the hum.
And plainly and more plainly
    Now through the gloom appears,
Far to left and far to right,
In broken gleams of dark-blue light,
The long array of helmets bright,
    The long array of spears.

And plainly and more plainly
    Now might the burghers know,
By port and vest, by horse and crest,
    Each warlike Lucomo.
There Cilnius of Arretium
    On his fleet roan was seen;
And Astur of the four-fold shield,
Girt with the brand none else may wield,
Tolumnius with the belt of gold,
And dark Verbenna from the hold
    By reedy Thrasymene.

And the Consul's brow was sad,
    And the Consul's speech was low,
And darkly looked he at the wall,
    And darkly at the foe.
"Their van will be upon us
    Before the bridge goes down;
And if they once may win the bridge,
    What hope to save the town?"

Then out spake brave Horatius,
  The Captain of the gate:
"To every man upon this earth
  Death cometh soon or late.
And how can man die better
  Than facing fearful odds,
For the ashes of his fathers
  And the temples of his Gods!

"Hew down the bridge, Sir Consul,
  With all the speed ye may;
I, with two more to help me,
  Will hold the foe in play.
In yon strait path a thousand
  May well be stopped by three.
Now who will stand on either hand,
  And keep the bridge with me?"

Then out spake Spurius Lartius;
  A Ramnian proud was he:
"Lo, I will stand at thy right hand,
  And keep the bridge with thee."
And out spake strong Herminius;
  Of Titian blood was he:
"I will abide on thy left side,
  And keep the bridge with thee."

"Horatius," quoth the Consul,
  "As thou sayest, so let it be."

And straight against that great array
  Forth went the dauntless Three.
For Romans in Rome's quarrel
  Spared neither land nor gold,
Nor son nor wife, nor limb nor life,
  In the brave days of old.

Now while the Three were tightening
  Their harness on their backs,
The Consul was the foremost man
  To take in hand an axe:
And Fathers mixed with Commons
  Seized hatchet, bar, and crow,
And smote upon the planks above,
  And loosed the props below.

Meanwhile the Tuscan army,
  Right glorious to behold,
Came flashing back the noonday light,
Rank behind rank, like surges bright
  Of a broad sea of gold.
Four hundred trumpets sounded
  A peal of warlike glee,
As that great host, with measured tread,
And spears advanced, and ensigns spread,
Rolled slowly towards the bridge's head,
  Where stood the dauntless Three.

The Three stood calm and silent
  And looked upon the foes,
And a great shout of laughter
  From all the vanguard rose:
And forth three chiefs came spurring
  Before that deep array;
To earth they sprang, their swords they drew,
And lifted high their shields, and flew
  To win the narrow way;

Aunus from green Tifernum,
  Lord of the Hill of Vines;
And Seius, whose eight hundred slaves
  Sicken in Ilva's mines;
And Picus, long to Clusium
  Vassal in peace and war,
Who led to fight his Umbrian powers
From that gray crag where, girt with towers,
The fortress of Nequinum lowers
  O'er the pale waves of Nar.

Stout Lartius hurled down Aunus
  Into the stream beneath:
Herminius struck at Seius,
  And clove him to the teeth:
At Picus brave Horatius
  Darted one fiery thrust;

And the proud Umbrian's gilded arms
   Clashed in the bloody dust.

Then Ocnus of Falerii
   Rushe on the Roman Three;
And Lausulus of Urgo,
   The rover of the sea;

And Aruns of Volsinium,
    Who slew the great wild boar,
The great wild boar that had his den
Amidst the reeds of Cosa's fen,
And wasted fields, and slaughtered men,
    Along Albinia's shore.

Herminius smote down Aruns:
    Lartius laid Ocnus low:
Right to the heart of Lausulus
    Horatius sent a blow.

"Lie there," he cried, "fell pirate!
No more, aghast and pale,
From Ostia's walls the crowd shall mark
The track of thy destroying bark.
No more Campania's hinds shall fly
To woods and caverns when they spy
Thy thrice accursed sail."

But now no sound of laughter
Was heard among the foes.
A wild and wrathful clamor
From all the vanguard rose.
Six spears' lengths from the entrance
Halted that deep array,
And for a space no man came forth
To win the narrow way.

But hark! the cry is Astur:
And lo! the ranks divide;
And the great Lord of Luna
Comes with his stately stride.
Upon his ample shoulders
Clangs loud the four-fold shield,
And in his hand he shakes the brand
Which none but he can wield.

He smiled on those bold Romans
A smile serene and high;

He eyed the flinching Tuscans,
    And scorn was in his eye.
Quoth he, "The she-wolf's litter
    Stand savagely at bay:
But will ye dare to follow,
    If Astur clears the way?"

Then, whirling up his broadsword
    With both hands to the height,
He rushed against Horatius,
    And smote with all his might.
With shield and blade Horatius
    Right deftly turned the blow.
The blow, though turned, came yet too nigh;
It missed his helm, but gashed his thigh:
The Tuscans raised a joyful cry
    To see the red blood flow.

He reeled, and on Herminius
    He leaned one breathing-space;
Then, like a wild cat mad with wounds,
    Sprang right at Astur's face.
Through teeth, and skull, and helmet,
    So fierce a thrust he sped,
The good sword stood a hand-breadth out
    Behind the Tuscan's head.

And the great Lord of Luna
  Fell at that deadly stroke,
As falls on Mount Alvernus
  A thunder-smitten oak.
Far o'er the crashing forest
  The giant arms lie spread;
And the pale augurs, muttering low,
  Gaze on the blasted head.

On Astur's throat Horatius
  Right firmly pressed his heels,
And thrice and four times tugged amain,
  Ere he wrenched out the steel.
"And see," he cried, "the welcome,
  Fair guests, that waits you here!
What noble Lucomo comes next,
  To taste our Roman cheer?"

But at this haughty challenge
  A sullen murmur ran,
Mingled of wrath, and shame, and dread,
  Along that glittering van.
There lacked not men of prowess,
  Nor men of lordly race;
For all Etruria's noblest
  Were round the fatal place.

But all Etruria's noblest
  Felt their hearts sink to see
On the earth the bloody corpses,
  In the path the dauntless Three:
And, from the ghastly entrance
  Where those bold Romans stood,
All shrank, like boys who unaware,
Ranging the wods to start a hare,
Come to the mouth of the dark lair
Where, growling low, a fierce old bear
  Lies amidst bones and blood.

Was none who would be foremost
  To lead such dire attack;
But those behind cried "Forward!"
  And those before cried "Back!"
And backward now and forward
  Wavers the deep array;
And on the tossing sea of steel,
To and fro the standards reel;
And the victorious trumpet-peal
  Dies fitfully away.

But meanwhile axe and lever
  Have manfuly been plied,
And now the bridge hangs tottering
  Above the boiling tide.
"Come back, come back, Horatius!"

Loud cried the Fathers all.
"Back, Lartius! back, Herminius!
　Back, ere the ruin fall!"

Back darted Spurius Lartius;
　Herminius darted back:
And, as they passed, beneath their feet
　They felt the timbers crack.
But when they turned their faces,
　And on the farther shore
Saw brave Horatius stand alone,
　They would have crossed once more.

But with a crash like thunder
  Fell every loosened beam,
And, like a dam, the mighty wreck
  Lay right athwart the stream:
And a long shout of triumph
  Rose from the walls of Rome,
As to the highest turret-tops
  Was splashed the yellow foam.

And, like a horse unbroken
  When first he feels the rein,
The furious river struggled hard,
  And tossed his tawny mane,
And burst the curb, and bounded,
  Rejoicing to be free,
And whirling down, in fierce career,
Battlement, and plank, and pier,
  Rushed headlong to the sea.

Alone stood brave Horatius,
    But constant still in mind;
Thrice thirty thousand foes before,
    And the broad flood behind.
"Down with him!" cried false Sextus,
    With a smile on his pale face.
"Now yield thee," cried Lars Porsena,
    "Now yield thee to our grace."

Round turned he, as not deigning
    Those craven ranks to see;
Naught spake he to Lars Porsena,
    To Sextus naught spake he:
But he saw on Palatinus
    The white porch of his home;
And he spake to the noble river
    That rolls by the towers of Rome.

"Oh, Tiber! Father Tiber!
    To whom the Romans pray,
A Roman's life, a Roman's arms,
    Take thou in charge this day!"
So he spake, and speaking sheathed
    The good sword by his side,
And with his harness on his back,
    Plunged headlong in the tide.

No sound of joy or sorrow
   Was heard from either bank;
But friends and foes in dumb surprise,
With parted lips and straining eyes,
   Stood gazing where he sank;
And when above the surges
   They saw his crest appear,
All Rome sent forth a rapturous cry,
And even the ranks of Tuscany
   Could scarce forbear to cheer.

But fiercely ran the current,
   Swollen high by months of rain:
And fast his blood was flowing;
   And he was sore in pain,
And heavy with his armor,
   And spent with changing blows:
And oft they thought him sinking,
   But still again he rose.

Never, I ween, did swimmer,
   In such an evil case,
Struggle through such a raging flood
   Safe to the landing-place:
But his limbs were borne up bravely
   By the brave heart within,
And our good Father Tiber
   Bare bravely up his chin.

"Curse on him!" quoth false Sextus:
  "Will not the villain drown?
But for this stay, ere close of day
  We should have sacked the town!"
"Heaven help him!" quoth Lars Porsena,
  "And bring him safe to shore;
For such a gallant feat of arms
  Was never seen before."

And now he feels the bottom;
  Now on dry earth he stands;
Now round him throng the Fathers
  To press his gory hands;
And now, with shouts and clapping,
  And noise of weeping loud,
He enters through the River-gate,
  Borne by the joyous crowd.

They gave him of the corn-land
  That was of public right
As much as two strong oxen
  Could plough from morn till night;
And they made a molten image,
  And set it up on high,
And there it stands unto this day
  To witness if I lie.

It stands in the Comitium,
  Plain for all folk to see;
Horatius in his harness,
  Halting upon one knee:
And underneath is written,
  In letters all of gold,
How valiantly he kept the bridge
  In the brave days of old.

*This is one of the great heroic poems of all time. What is
presented in these pages is an abridgement of the full poem.
The original comprises many, many more verses. The poem
is filled with oft-quoted lines, such as:*

*And how can men die better than facing fearful odds
For the ashes of their fathers and the temples of their Gods.*

    *Macaulay has succeeded in raising before our eyes the
stirring world of Rome with its spirited, martial peoples.
Only a scholar thoroughly versed in the classics could mar-
shal such an array of references and place names, and impart so fully the feeling of the times.*
    *Note the change of rhythm in some of the long stanzas
where added lines gradually build up the verse to a full
crescendo, like the rolling of a drum.*

CHARLES GODFREY LELAND (1824-1903)

Born in Philadelphia, the son of a wealthy merchant,
Leland abandoned the profession of law in favor of jour-
nalism. He traveled extensively abroad, always writing
books on unpredictable topics. But it was through his humorous ballads that he won literary fame.

The Ballad of Charity

It was in a pleasant depot, sequestered from the rain,
That many weary passengers were waiting
        for the train;
Piles of quite expensive baggage, many a
        gorgeous portmanteau,
Ivory-handled umberellas made a most touristic show.

Whereunto there came a person, very humble
        was his mien,
Who took an observation of the interesting scene;
Closely scanned the umberellas, watched with joy
        the mighty trunks,
And observed that all the people were securing
        Pullman bunks.

Who was followed shortly after by a most
        unhappy tramp,
Upon whose features Poverty had jounced her
        iron stamp;
And to make a clear impression as bees sting
        while they buzz,
She had hit him rather harder than she
        generally does.

For he was so awfully ragged, and in parts
        so awfully bare,
That the folks were quite repulsioned to behold him
        begging there;
And instead of drawing currency from out of their
        pocket-books,
They drew themselves asunder with aversionary looks.

Sternly gazed the first newcomer on the
        unindulgent crowd,
Then in tones which pierced the depot he
        sololicussed aloud:—
"I have traveled o'er this continent from Quebec
        to Saginaw,
But such a set of scalawags as these I never saw!

"You are wealthy, you are loaded, you have houses,
        lands and rent,
Yet unto a suffering mortal, you will not donate a cent;

You expend your missionaries all the way
        to Timbuktu,
But there isn't any heathen that is half as small as you.

"You are lucky—you have check-books and
        deposits in the bank,
And ye squanderate your money like titled
        folks of rank;
The onyx and the sardonyx upon your garments shine,
And you drink cocktails at dinner and wash them
        down with wine.

"You are going for the summer to the islands
        by the sea,
Where a sandwich sells for two bucks, and it's
        fifty cents for tea;

Ivory-handled umberellas do not come into my plan,
But I can give some comfort to my suffering
     fellow man.

"Handbags made of alligator are not truly at my call,
Yet in the eyes of Mercy, I am richer than you all,
For I can give five dollars where you cannot
     stand a dime,
And never miss it neither, nor regret it any time."

Saying this he drew a wallet from inside his fancy vest,
And gave the tramp a V-note which it was
     his level best;
Other people having seen him, soon to
     charity inclined—

One genuine real giver makes a hundred change
        their mind.

The first who gave five dollars led the other one about,
And at every contribution, he a-raised a joyful shout;
Exclaiming how 'twas noble to relieviate distress,
And remarking that our duty is our present happiness.

Eight hundred bucks in greenbacks were collected
        by the tramp,
When he bid them all good evening, and went out
        into the damp;
And was followed briefly after by the one who
        made the speech,
And who showed by good example how to
        practise as to preach.

Which soon around the corner the couple quickly met,
And the tramp produced the specie for to
        liquidate his debt;
And the man who did the preaching took five
        hundred of the sum,
Which five from eight collected left three hundred
        for the bum.

And the couple passed the summer at the seashore
        with the rest;
Greatly changed in their appearance and most
        elegantly dressed.

Any fowl with change of feathers may a brilliant
      bird become:
Oh, how hard is life for many! Oh, how sweet
      it is for some!

In this fine spoof, the author evokes misplaced sympathy.
    *The poet hints that he is spoofing by his use of certain
manufactured words. We are told that the onlookers were
quite "repulsioned" (instead of repulsed), that the burghers
"squanderate" their money (instead of squander), and that
the speaker "solilicussed" (instead of soliliquized). The poet,
in his own delightful way, is letting us know that the man
who exaggerates and corrupts the language is very likely to
exaggerate and corrupt the facts. Evidently, something
phony is going on.*

ERNST LAWRENCE THAYER (1863-1940)

In 1888, Thayer, an American newspaper man, wrote *Casey at the Bat* for the San Francisco Examiner. The poem achieved country-wide fame, and has been reprinted again and again.

Casey at the Bat

It looked extremely rocky for the Mudville nine
    that day,
The score stood two to four with just one inning
    left to play;
And so, when Cooney died at first, and Burrows
    did the same,
A sickly silence fell upon the patrons of the game.

A straggling few got up to go in deep despair.
    The rest
Clung to the hope that springs eternal within
    each human breast;
They thought if only Casey could but get a whack
    at that—
They'd put up *even money* now, with Casey
    at the bat.
But Flynn preceded Casey, and so did Jimmy Blake,

And the former was a washout, and the latter
        was a fake;
So upon that stricken multitude grim Melancholy sat,
For there seemed but little chance of Casey's
        getting to the bat.

But Flynn let drive a single to the wonderment of all,
And Blake whom all had sneered at, tore
        the cover off the ball;
And when the dust had lifted, and they saw what
        had occurred,
There was Jimmy safe on second and Flynn
        a-huggin' third!

Then from the gladdened multitude went up
        a joyous yell,
It rumbled in the mountaintops, it rattled in the dell,
It struck upon the hillside and rebounded on the flat;
For Casey, mighty Casey, was advancing to the bat.

There was ease in Casey's manner as he stepped
        into his place,
There was pride in Casey's bearing, and a smile
        on Casey's face;
And when, responding to the cheers, he lightly
        doffed his hat,
No stranger in the crowd could doubt 'twas
        Casey at the bat.

Ten thousand eyes were upon him as he rubbed
      his hands with dirt;
Five thousand tongues applauded when he wiped
      them on his shirt.
Then while the writhing pitcher ground the ball
      into his hip,
Defiance gleamed in Casey's eye, a sneer
      curled Casey's lip.

And now the leather-covered sphere came hurtling
      through the air,
And Casey stood a-watching it in haughty
      grandeur there;

Close by the sturdy batsman the ball unheeded sped:
"That ain't my style," said Casey. "Strike one!" the
      umpire said.

From the benches, black with people, there went up
      a muffled roar,
Like the beating of the storm-waves on a stern
      and distant shore;
"Kill him! Kill the umpire!" shouted someone
      in the stands.
And it's sure they would have killed him had not
      Casey raised his hand.

With a smile of Christian charity great Casey's
      visage shone;

He stilled the rising tumult; he bade the game go on;
He signalled to the pitcher, and once more
      the spheroid flew,
But Casey still ignored it; and the umpire said,
      "Strike two!"

"Fraud!" cried the maddened thousands, and
      the echo answered "Fraud!"
But one scornful look from Casey and the audience
      was awed;
They saw his face grow stern and cold, they saw
      his muscles strain.
And they knew that Casey wouldn't let that ball
      go by again.

The sneer is gone from Casey's lip, his teeth
      are clenched with hate;
He pounds with cruel violence his bat upon the plate;
And now the pitcher holds the ball, and now
      he lets it go.
And now the air is shattered by the force
      of Casey's blow.

Oh, somewhere in this favored land the sun
      is shining bright;
The band is playing somewhere, and somewhere
      hearts are light;

And somewhere men are laughing, and somewhere
    children shout;
But there is no joy in Mudville—*mighty Casey*
    has struck out!

This poem has become an American classic. See how the poet builds up Casey's arrogance:

"Defiance gleamed in Casey's eye, a sneer curled Casey's lip;"
"And Casey stood a-watching it in haughty grandeur there."

    This all leads up to Casey's ignominious failure, which the poet dramatically reserves for the very last sentence.

ANONYMOUS

Casey—Twenty Years After

The Mudville team was desperate in that big
    championship game;
The chances were they'd bite the dust and kiss
    goodbye to Fame;
Three men were hurt and two were benched;
    the score stood six to four.
They had to make three big, big runs in just
    two innings more.

"It can't be done," the captain said, a pallor
    on his face;
"I've got two has-beens in the field, a jerk
    on second base;
And should another man get spiked or crippled
    in some way,
The team could sure be counted out, with only
    eight to play.

"We're up against it anyhow, as far as I can see;
My boys ain't hitting like they should, and that's
    what worries me;

The luck's all with the other side; the pennant
    we can't win;
It's mighty tough! There's nought to do but
    take it on the chin."

The eighth round opened: one, two, three—
    the enemy went down;
But Mudville went out quite the same. The captain
    wore a frown.
The first half of the ninth came round, two men had
    been called out,
When Mudville's catcher broke a thumb, and
    could not go the route.

A melancholy silence fell on the crowd
    assembled there.
Defeat, defeat was what all sensed! Defeat hung
    in the air!
With only eight men in the field, 'twould be a
    gruesome fray;
Small wonder that the captain cursed the day
    he learned to play.

"Lend me a man to finish with," he begged the
    other team;
"Lend you a man?" the foe replied; "My boy,
    you're in a dream!

We want that dear old pennant, pal." And then,
      a final jeer—
"There's only one thing you can do—
      call for a volunteer."

The captain stood and pondered in a listless sort
      of way;
He never was a quitter and wouldn't quit today.
"Is there within the grandstand here"— his voice
      rang loud and clear—
"A man who has the sporting blood to be a volunteer?"

A sense of death now settled o'er that sickly multitude;
Despair rode wild and rampant; you couldn't
      mistake the mood.
The captain stood with cap in hand, and
      hopeless was his glance,
And then a big old man cried out, "Say, Cap,
      I'll take a chance!"

Into the field he bounded with a step both
      firm and light;
"Give me the mask and mitt," he said. "Let's get in
      there and fight!
The game is not beyond recall; a winner you
      have found;
Although I'm ancient, I'm a brute and muscular
      and sound."

His hair was sprinkled here and there with little
    streaks of gray;
Around his eyes and on his brow, a bunch of
    wrinkles lay.
The captain smiled despairingly, and slowly
    turned away.
"Why, he's all right," one rooter yelled. "C'mon,
    Cap, let him play!"
"All right, go on," the captain sighed. The stranger
    turned around,
Took off his coat—and collar, too—and threw them
    on the ground.
The humor of the situation semed to hit them
    one and all,
And as the stranger donned his mask, the
    umpire yelled, "Play ball!"

Three balls the pitcher at him hurled, three balls of
    lightning speed;
The oldster caught them all with ease and did not
    seem to heed.
Each ball had been pronounced a strike, the side
    had been put out,
And as he walked in towards the bench, he heard
    the rooters shout.

One Mudville boy went out on strikes, and one was
    killed at first;

The captain saw his hopes all dashed, and
    gnashed his teeth and cursed.
But the next man smashed a double; and the
    fourth man swatted clear;
And in a thunder of applause, came the
    volunteer.

His feet were planted in the earth, he swung a
    warlike club;
The captain saw his awkward pose, and softly
    whispered, "Dub!"
The pitcher looked at him and grinned, then
    heaved a speedy pill—
And the echo of that fearful swat still lingers
    with us still.

High, fast and far that spheroid flew; it sailed and
     sailed away;
It ne'er was found, so it's supposed it still floats
     on today.
Three runs came in, the pennant would be
     Mudville's for a year;
And fans and players gathered round to cheer
     the volunteer.

"What's your name?" the captain asked. "Tell us
	your name!" cried all;
And down the unknown's cheeks great tears in
	rivulets did fall.
For one brief moment he was still, then murmured
	soft and low:
"I'm mighty Casey who struck out—just twenty
	years ago!"

*This anonymously written saga is a beautiful take-off on the
original Casey poem. Twenty years later the big bluffer
finally redeems himself.*

Ivan Skavinsky Skavar

The sons of the Prophet are brave men and bold,
   And quite unaccustomed to fear;
But the bravest by far, in the ranks of the Shah,
   Was Abdul Abulbul Amir.

If you wanted a man to encourage the van,
   Or harass the foe from the rear,
Storm fort or redoubt, you had only to shout
   For Abdul Abulbul Amir.

Now the heroes were plenty and well known to fame,
   In the troops that were led by the Czar,
And the bravest of these was a man by the name
   Of Ivan Skavinsky Skavar.

He could jump fifty yards and tell fortunes at cards,
   And strum on the Spanish guitar,
In fact quite the cream of the Muscovite team
   Was Ivan Skavinsky Skavar.

One day this bold Russian, he shouldered his gun
   And donned his most insolent sneer,
Downtown he did go, where he trod on the toe
   Of Abdul Abulbul Amir.

"Young man," Abdul roared, "with your life are
     you bored?

Do you wish to end your career?
Vile infidel, know, you have trod on the toe
    Of Abdul Abulbul Amir!

"So take your last look at sunshine and brook,
    And send your regrets to the Czar—
For by this I imply, you are going to die,
    Count Ivan Skavinsky Skavar!"

Then this bold Mameluke drew his trusty skibouk,
    Singing "Allah Il Allah! Al-hah"
And with murd'rous intent, he ferociously went,
    For Ivan Skavinsky Skavar.

They parried and thrust, they side-stepped
        and cussed,
    Of blood they both spilled a great part;
For they both were so tough, so strong and so rough—
    'Twas a wonderful fight from the start!

They fought all that night 'neath the pale
        yellow moon;
    The din it was heard from afar,
And huge multitudes came, so great was the fame,
    Of Abdul and Ivan Skavar.

As Abdul's long knife was exacting the life,
    In fact, he was shouting "Huzzah!"

He felt himself struck by the wily Kalmuck,
　Count Ivan Skavinsky Skavar.

The Sultan rode by in his red-breasted fly,
　Expecting the victor to cheer,
But as he drew nigh he heard the last sigh
　Of Abdul Abulbul Amir.

There's a tomb rises up where the Bosphorus rolls,
　And carved there in characters clear,
Is, "Stranger, when passing, oh pray for the soul
　Of Abdul Abulbul Amir."

In a Muscovite town 'long the Volga's green banks,
  "Neath the light of the cold Northern Star,
A maid tends the grave of her hero so brave,
  Ivan Skavinsky Skavar!

Take a close look at each hero. The Turk is a great fighter;
he can lead in battle or defend well in the rearguard; he
can storm a large fort, or envelop a small station.

What are Ivan's skills? Well, he's a good jumper; he
tells fortunes; and he's a good guitar player.

No, they are not evenly matched. Moreover, it is Ivan
who has the unpleasant sneer on his face and who starts
up the whole fracas; he's just looking for trouble. He insults
the Turk by stomping on his toe—not a very crucial issue for
a test of national honor.

In the fight, the poet is spoofing not only epic battles
but all poets who ever wrote epics. Multitudes have gath-
ered to watch; even the Sultan himself has taken the royal
buggy to ride hundreds of miles to view the historic en-
counter.

What is the anonymous poet really saying? That the
heroes are not so heroic, and that the mighty Russian nation
is not so mighty. And most important, that poetry can be
sheer fun.

Look at inner rhymes like "this bold Mameluke drew
his trusty skibouk" and "he felt himself struck by the wily
Kalmuck." Are they not delightfully clever!

The Goat and the Three Red Shirts

There was a man, now please to note,
There was a man, who had a goat;
He loved that goat, indeed he did,
He loved that goat, just like a kid.

One day that goat felt frisk and fine,
Ate three red shirts from off the line.
The man he grabbed him by the back,
And tied him to a railroad track.

But when the train hove into sight,
That goat grew pale and green with fright.
He heaved a sigh, as if in pain,
Coughed up those shirts and flagged the train!

A perceptive reader would suspect that some joke was in store upon spotting the pun, "He loved that goat, just like a kid."

Rather startling the use that goat made of those three red shirts!

HART

PUBLISHING

COMPANY